# Malaysian Butterflies

Dedicated To....

....My Parents

# Malaysian Butterflies
## ~ an introduction

YONG HOI-SEN

TROPICAL PRESS SDN. BHD.

TROPICAL PRESS SDN. BHD.
29 JALAN RIONG
59100 KUALA LUMPUR
MALAYSIA

First Impression    1983
Second Impression   1984
Third Impression    1986
Fourth Impression   1989

ISBN 967–73–0017–2

TYPESET, COLOUR SEPARATED,
PRINTED AND BOUND BY ART PRINTING WORKS SDN. BHD.
29, JALAN RIONG, 59100 KUALA LUMPUR, MALAYSIA

# Contents

# Preface

MALAYSIA'S 130 million year-old rainforest houses one of the world's richest and unique animal treasures. Although the country is made up of two distinct geographical regions, the fauna of Peninsular Malaysia and East Malaysia (Sabah and Sarawak) are similar though by no means identical. For instance, about 87 % of the 1008 species of butterflies recorded in Peninsular Malaysia are found in East Malaysia. Many of Malaysia's butterflies also occur in neighbouring countries from Sri Lanka and India to southern China and Philippines and south to Sulawesi.

About half of the country's butterfly fauna are to be found in the lowland below about 750 metres in altitude. Those that live only on the hills above 750 metres a.s.l. comprise only about one-seventh of the total. The remainder occur both in the lowland and the hills.

The majority of Malaysia's butterflies live in the primeval forest. These species are represented by comparatively few individuals. On the other hand, the few widely distributed species occur in large numbers and frequent secondary plant associations.

Three basic books have been written about the butterflies of Peninsular Malaysia. Of these, *The butterflies of the Malay Peninsula* by A.S. Corbet and H.M. Pendlebury as revised by J.N. Eliot (Kuala Lumpur: Malayan Nature Society, 1978) is the standard reference and is indispensable for the serious students of butterflies. *Butterflies of West Malaysia and Singapore* by W.A. Fleming (Kuala Lumpur: Longman, 1974) is essentially a field guide as well as an identification aid. In contrast, *Common Malayan butterflies* by R. Morrell (Kuala Lumpur: Longmans, 1960) is for the beginner but unfortunately has not been revised since it was written more than 20 years ago. All three books, however, do not contain pictures of living butterflies. Furthermore, the photographers would find it difficult to identify some of their pictures on the common butterflies.

The aim of the present book is to give a simple illustrated account of the butterfly fauna of Malaysia in particular and to the world of butterfly in general. The choice of the material here presented, depends on what I think may be of general interest, the availability of illustrations (colour pictures), and the limitation of space.

Most Skipper butterflies are very hard to identify and many are crepuscular, hence not usually encountered. As such only few examples are represented. Similarly, the identification of many Lycaenid butterflies requires the services of the specialist.

The zoological and technical terminology has been kept to a minimum. On the other hand, although the common names of many species are available, the Latin or scientific names of butterflies are also used throughout to avoid confusion and ambiguity as they are used by writers and speakers of all languages.

I hope this book may prove interesting reading to a variety of people from different walks of life and from different lands. It is hoped that it will stimulate more people, particularly the school children, to take an interest in the great variety of butterflies. It is also hoped that the colour illustrations of living butterflies will help readers who wish to identify these insects in their natural environs.

The information presented in this book comes from many sources—from books, journals, colleagues and hours of wandering in the primeval forest. All the pictures included in this book have been taken by the author over a number of years.

Last but not least, I wish to express my indebtedness to all those from whom I have learned and benefitted much. In particular, I wish to thank Royal Professor Ungku A. Aziz (Vice-Chancellor, University of Malaya), Professor Ahmad Nawawi (Deputy Vice-Chancellor), and Professor S.S. Dhaliwal (Dean of Science) for various facilities and encouragement, Dr S.G. Khoo for his valuable comments, and Mrs Peggy Azavedo for typing the manuscript.

September 1981                    H.S. Yong

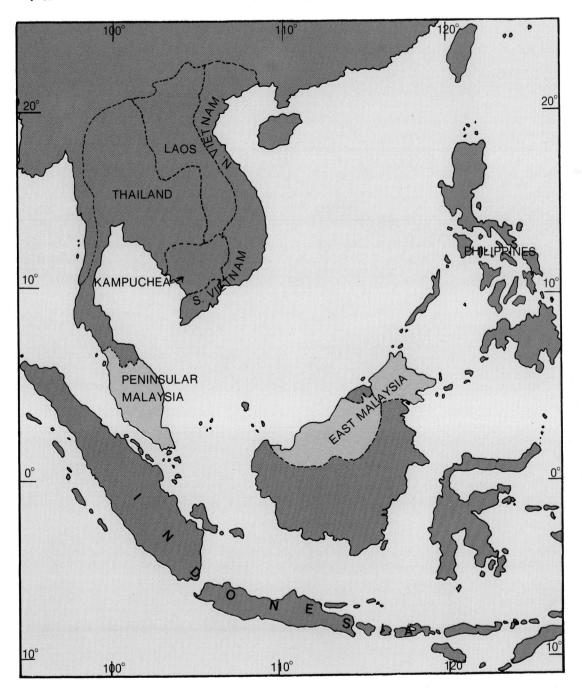

# INTRODUCTION

Plain Lacewing *Cethosia penthesilea*

# Butterflies:
# The Most Glamorous of Insects

**B**UTTERFLIES are frail creatures of indescribable beauty. Their glowing, brilliant colours and patterns are without doubt their claim to fame in the world of humans. As early as 300 B.C., the Chinese philosopher Chuang Tzu wrote of them, "I do not know whether I was then a man dreaming I was a butterfly, or whether I am now a butterfly dreaming I am a man."

According to American–Indian legend, butterflies were created for the delight of mankind when the Great Spirit breathed life into the myriad coloured pebbles of the shimmering streams and gave them wings so that they could display the gentle beauties of nature. Indeed, of all insects, butterflies are the most glamorous and beautiful and appeal most to our poetic senses.

Male Rajah Brooke's Birdwings congregating to drink at a puddle by the side of a waterfall near Bukit Tinggi, Pahang.

Butterflies are figured in numerous folklore and legends—as symbol of longevity, good fortune or evil, as insignia of fire gods or authority, and as the departed souls of men. However, there is no mention of butterflies in the Bible although moths are referred to as an example of bad things.

With the exception of the Polar regions and other areas with extreme temperatures, butterflies are to be found almost everywhere on dry land. In Malaysia, more than 1000 species have been recorded and more new species are expected to be discovered. The first documented collection in this country dates back to 1779. These specimens, collected by Danish surgeon John Gerard Koenig, are preserved in the Banks Collection in the British Museum or in the Copenhagen Museum (the collection of Tønder-Lund and Schestedt). Other notable collectors included Thomas Stamford Raffles and Alfred Russel

Wallace. A few Malaysian species, *e.g.* Rajah Brooke's Birdwing, are so beautiful and remarkable that they are famous the world over.

There are many people who appreciate butterflies merely for their beauty while others study them in scientific depth. As many of Malaysia's finest butterflies have the habit of sitting with wings erect and sucking up liquid from a muddy spot or from animal dung by the roadside, they can be easily approached and photographed or captured. The excitement of such a pursuit is perhaps best and most vividly described by A.R. Wallace, the distinguished author of *The Malay Archipelago,* "The beauty and brilliance of this insect are indescribable, and none but a naturalist can understand the intense excitement I experienced when I at length caught it. On taking it out of my net and opening the glorious wings, my heart began to beat violently, the blood rushed to my head, and I felt much more like fainting, than I have done in apprehension of immediate death. I had a headache the rest of the day, so great was the excitement produced by what will appear to most people a very inadequate cause."

*Eurema sari* at moist seepage.

# What is a Butterfly?

THE name butterfly is derived from the name butter-coloured fly given possibly to the bright-yellow Brimstone butterfly (*Gonepteryx rhamni*) of northern Europe, which in olden days, being the first to appear in Spring thus proclaiming the dawn of warmth and sunshine and the departure of the hardships of winter, was greatly welcomed by the people. A precise definition of a butterfly involves a detailed examination of the venation of the wings and other body parts.

In general, butterflies are insects belonging to the order Lepidoptera in which the two pairs of wings as well as the legs and body are covered with scales. They have a coiled proboscis which is used for sucking liquid foods such as nectar from flowers. Their mandibles or chewing mouthparts are imperfect or totally absent.

It was Carl von Linne (better known as Linnaeus) who first called butterflies (and moths) 'Lepidoptera', from the Greek words *lepis* (a scale) and *pteron* (wing), meaning 'scale-wing'. The Lepidopterans are normally divided into butterflies and moths.

Most butterflies are day fliers whereas moths are generally nocturnal in habit. Butterflies generally rest with their wings closed in an upright position above the body, whereas moths rest with their wings

Lime Butterfly *Papilio demoleus*.

Atlas Moth *Attacus atlas*.

held in a horizontal or roof-like position. The antennae or feelers of butterflies are threadlike and the tips are distinctly or gradually thickened to form a club. On the other hand, the antennae of moths are feathery or they may be threadlike without a club. Many moths have a bristle (or a group of bristles) known as the frenulum at the base of the anterior margin of the hindwing, whereas butterflies do not possess a frenulum.

Although the characters listed above are generally adequate for distinguishing between butterflies and moths, there are as in the rules of grammar in a language, exceptions to these characteristics. Further, the butterflies as traditionally delimited may be divided into the 'true butterflies' and the 'Skipper butterflies'; it is indeed now advocated by some specialists that the Skippers should not be properly constituted as butterflies.

The Skippers differ from the true butterflies in that: (1) their antennae are usually hooked at the tip and are set widely at the base, (2) they fly with a jerky or skipping action, and (3) they rest with the forewings usually held closed together over the thorax and with the hindwings open and flat.

Skipper butterfly

Swallow-tailed Moth *Lyssa zampa*.

# Life History of Butterflies

**D**URING their life-cycles butterflies undergo complete metamorphosis ('change of form'), that is, they pass through four distinct stages, *viz.* the ovum or egg, the larva or caterpillar, the pupa or chrysalis, and the imago or adult.

Adult butterflies live for about two or three weeks. The newly emerged female can attract a mate from miles away by scent. The record appears to be a distance of about 11 kilometres.

The female butterfly discharges minute fractions of scent molecules into the air. The males are attracted by these scent molecules known as sex attractants. Likewise, the males have scent scales on their wings, or glandular scales or hairs on their bodies, wings or legs, which are able to produce aphrodisiac scents during courtship.

1. THE EGG.  When mating has taken place, the female butterfly lays her eggs on the leaf surface of a specific food plant; each species of butterflies has its particular group or species of food plants. The eggs are usually laid singly, but in some species, they are laid in clusters. The end opposite to the micropyle (a minute opening through which the sperm has entered the egg) is attached to the leaf by means of a sticky secretion. The total number of eggs laid may range from about 20 to 200.

The eggs are generally white, pale yellow or greenish in colour, and the surface is often sculptured. They may be spherical, cylindrical or flask-shaped. Each family or subfamily of butterflies usually has a characteristic structure of the egg. The eggs of the Birdwing and Swallowtail butterflies (Family Papilionidae) are spherical to dome-shaped, and without prominent sculpturing. Those of the White and Sulphur butterflies (Family Pieridae) are flask-shaped with longitudinal ridges, and those of the Nymphalidae and related group of

Life history of *Elymnias hypermnestra*.

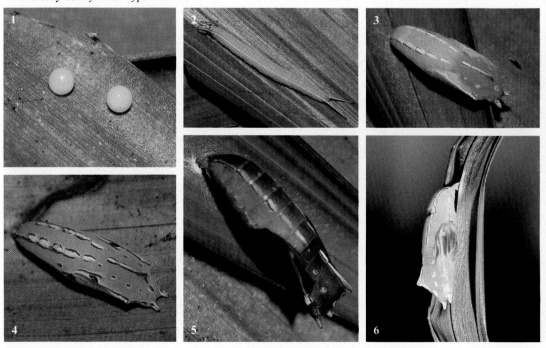

families are melon-shaped, usually flattened at one or both ends and often prominently ridged or spined. In contrast, the eggs of Lycaenidae and Hesperiidae may be very diverse.

2. THE CATERPILLAR. The egg hatches into the caterpillar in about two or more days. The caterpillar is very different in appearance from the adult butterfly. It has powerful jaws and feeds on green leaves, and

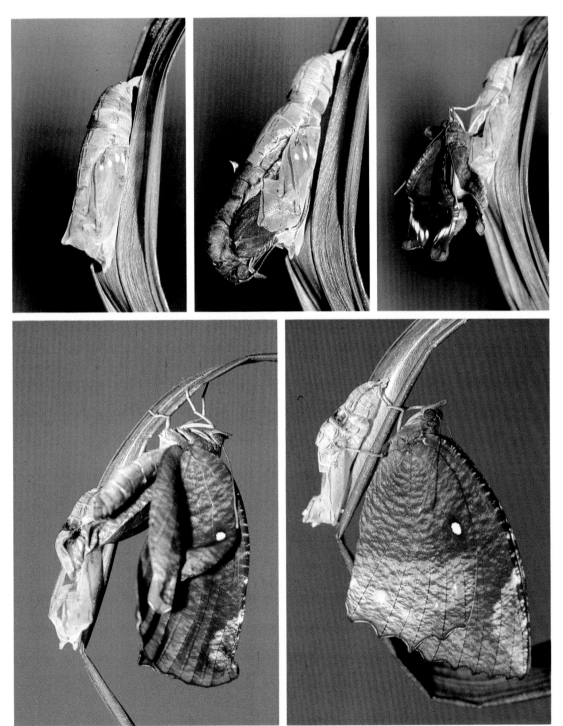

may cause great damage when it is present in large number.

Caterpillars of butterflies are variable in form, but those of a particular family exhibit characteristic features, such as presence of tubercles, spines or hairs.

The young caterpillar usually consumes the empty egg shell as its first meal. Then it feeds intensively on the leaves of the food plant, and grows very rapidly during the process. As its outer skin is fairly rigid, the caterpillar moults (casting of the skin to allow growth) about 4 or 5 times before it achieves full size in about 2–8 weeks.

When the caterpillar has reached its last larval instar (an instar is the stage between moults), it seeks out a suitable spot and then sheds its final skin and turns into a chrysalis.

3. THE CHRYSALIS. During this apparently dormant stage, the larval body structure breaks down and reforms itself to become the adult butterfly.

There is great variation in the chrysalis of different species of butterflies. They may be brown, green, or metallic silver and gold in colour.

The chrysalis attaches itself to the silken pad produced by the caterpillar by means of a pointed hooked projection (called cremaster), formed on the last abdominal segment of the caterpillar. It usually assumes either an upside down position (as in the Danaidae, Satyridae and Nymphalidae), or an upright position with an additional girdle of silk around the middle for support (as in the Papilionidae and Pieridae). In the Skipper butterflies the chrysalis is usually enclosed in a cocoon or rests between curled-up leaves drawn together by silken threads.

After a period of one to several weeks, the transformation will be completed and the adult butterfly is ready to emerge. This is indicated by the chrysalis taking on an oily transparency and the colours of the wings may show through the once opaque skin. The chrysalis splits along the dorsal surface and the adult butterfly gradually works its way out.

4. THE ADULT BUTTERFLY. It is usually in the early morning that the adult butterfly emerges from the split skin of the chrysalis. It emerges wet, with small limp and crumpled wings. When free of the pupal case, it crawls upwards to a supporting surface so that the wings can hang down and develop normally. This is achieved by pumping its body fluid into the veins in the wings.

As soon as they are fully expanded which takes about an hour, the wings are opened and closed a few times before any attempt is made at flight. When the wings are completely dry, the butterfly takes off to find itself food and a mate.

The adult butterfly feeds on exposed fluids such as nectar from flowers, sap from tree trunks, moisture from the soil, animal droppings, and the exudates from rotting vegetable or animal matter. When feeding, the tubular proboscis (often called the tongue and usually coiled like a watchspring beneath the head) is uncoiled instantly and thrust deep into the source of liquid food. Although the antennae are the chief organs of smell, the sense of taste that causes the uncoiling of the proboscis, is not located at the head but on the soles of the feet.

At all stages of the life history, butterflies are preyed upon by birds, spiders and other predatory animals. The caterpillars and chrysalids are frequently attacked by flies and wasps as well as a variety of other predators and parasites. These creatures act as a natural check on the caterpillar population explosion which would cause serious damage to the particular food plant.

As they have practically no means of fleeing from their predators or fighting back, the caterpillars resort to a great variety of passive defensive specialisations. Their bodies may be grotesquely shaped or armed with spines or other projections. Some may possess special organs that protrude out from the head and emit strong, repellent scents when the caterpillars are disturbed or attacked. Some may even resemble a bird-dropping, part of a leaf or leaf-stalk, or other creations of Nature.

Adult butterflies also exhibit a great variety of defense mechanisms. Among them, 'warning coloration' and 'flash coloration' are perhaps the commonest. For example, the Danaids advertise their unpleasant taste by yellow and black or blue-black and white colours. This protective adaptation is mimicked by other butterflies which are 'wholesome' in taste. However, the most famous of all is perhaps the leaf-like appearance of the Leaf Butterfly.

*Euploea mulciber* caught and eaten by a web spider.

# Butterfly Watching

BUTTERFLIES are acclaimed worldwide to be the most magnificent of all insects. Their total beauty, however, can never be adequately conveyed through colour prints or preserved specimens. There is indeed no substitute for seeing the real living butterfly in its natural environment.

In contrast to 'bird-watching' which commands a good following, the hobby of 'butterfly watching' is not so well promoted. Butterfly watching is in fact as rewarding, if not more so than bird-watching. Indeed, one who takes up this hobby will never cease to be astonished and delighted by the great array of camouflage, mimicry and other protective devices that are to be found in the adult butterflies as well as their early stages. In the course of time, one also acquires a knowledge of the flowering plants that the butterflies visit, the food plants of the caterpillars, the enemies of the butterflies, and a multitude of other information pertaining to nature.

Butterflies are to be found in nearly every habitat on land. Different habitats, however, are frequented by different kinds of butterflies. In general, they are most easily observed in gardens and along roadsides, as well as along paths, clearings and streams in the forest, and on mountain and hill tops. The best starting place for butterfly watching is perhaps one's own garden and roadsides near one's home. In addition to easy access, this approach also affords one to watch the butterflies throughout the year, and hence useful information on butterfly

Chestnut Tiger *Parantica sita* at the hill top of Cameron Highlands, Pahang.

▲ Common Sergeant *Athyma perius* by the waywide at
Selama, Perak.

▼ *Troides amphrysus* at Poring, Sabah.

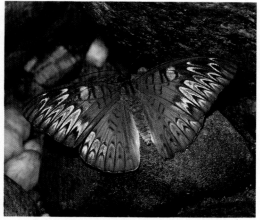

▲ *Tanaecia palguna* at Taman Negara, Pahang.

◄ *Symbrenthia* sp at Ulu Langat
Forest Reserve, Selangor.

▼ *Graphium evemon* congregating at a muddy
spot.

biology can be gathered.

For the outdoor-loving, one may station oneself in the shade near forest stream or near flowering plants and await the butterflies to parade themselves. For this sedentary approach, one may also set baits to attract the butterflies. Those more energetic may trek through the forest to search for other kinds of butterflies that do not or seldom come to the open.

Most species of butterflies are most active in mid-morning (8–10 a.m.) and late afternoon (3–5 p.m.). They usually stay in the treetops or rest in the shade in between these active feeding periods. Some species (*e.g.* certain Satyrines), however, are active at dawn or at dusk, while some others (*e.g.* certain Amathusiids) are only active at dawn.

Male and female butterflies are not often found together. Indeed, the males of some species often congregate with other species rather than with their own females, at moist spots on forest roads and on sand banks by rivers and streams, where larger animals have come to drink and have contaminated the sand with their urine.

Many butterflies are attracted to various animal and vegetable matter, and hence can be lured with such substances. The animal matter attractive to butterflies includes the faeces and urine of both humans and wild animals. The best of all, however, are said to be tiger and panther dung! Some butterflies are also attracted to carrion and decaying fish or prawns.

Among plant matter, the partly dried Indian Heliotrope (*Heliotropium indicum*) appears to be magically effective for many Danaid butterflies. Some Satyrines, most Amathusiids and some Nymphalids are fond of rotting fruit, such as banana, papaya and pineapple.

In the pursuit of butterfly watching it is inevitable that one needs to collect specimens for identification, reference or other purposes. This is to be encouraged, but the collecting of many duplicates should be avoided and commercial collecting should be curtailed.

The thrills and unexpected adventures of butterfly watching cannot be adequately conveyed in words to those who have not experienced them. Even for those initiated, each time they return to the same location they may find some new species which they have missed previously. Furthermore, butterfly watching enables us to learn to see, to sense, to thrill and above all to appreciate and to cherish our very own splendid natural heritage.

Malay Lacewing *Cethosia hypsea.*

# BUTTERFLIES
# PARADE

*Pathysa antiphates*          *Appias lyncida*

*Polyura jalysus*

# Family Papilionidae

MEMBERS of this family of butterflies are generally referred to as Swallowtails because of the semblance of their long and pointed fore-wings to a swallow's and the possession by many members of slender 'tails' projecting from their hindwings. Many of the tropical members are, however, tailless and are commonly known as Birdwings. These butterflies are of worldwide occurrence, and are the best known and most popular of all the butterflies. They include some of the most magnificent and spectacular butterflies.

Only one subfamily (Papilioninae) of Swallowtail butterflies is represented in this part of the world. Most members of this group are forest or woodland butterflies. Many of them are quite common, both on the hills and at lower elevations. They are large in size and strong on the wing. When feeding, the forewings in many species can be observed to flutter rather quickly (to maintain balance) while the hindwings are kept fairly still.

In general the two sexes are similar, but there are cases of sexual dimorphism, and in a few species the female butterfly is polymorphic. The males of some species are attracted to damp muddy spots along roads or trails and to seepages on roads or river-

*Papilio fuscus* and *Paranticopsis delessertii* drinking at a sandy seepage.

banks. Their female counterparts, however, rarely join these 'mud-puddle or seepage clubs'.

All six legs in the adult butterfly are well developed and fit for walking. The pupae are always upright and supported by a silken girdle. The caterpillars possess an eversible fleshy forked process situated behind the head. When the caterpillar is threatened or disturbed, this organ (the osmeterium) is dramatically thrushed out through a slit on the thorax and produces a pungent scent. This is considered to be a protective device chiefly against the parasitic insects or predators.

The food plant includes species of Annonaceae, Aristolochiaceae, Lauraceae, and Umbelliferae. The caterpillars which feed on poisonous or distasteful food plant are able to pass on food toxins to the adult butterfly which is then chemically protected against predators.

A Papilionid caterpillar displaying its forked osmeterium when alarmed.

A characteristic pose of a Papilionid pupa, attached to the citrus plant by a silk girdle.

*Graphium eurypylus* and *Paranticopsis macareus* (Lesser Zebra) drinking by a river bank.

# *Trogonoptera brookiana* (Wallace)

## RAJAH BROOKE'S BIRDWING

This butterfly was first discovered in 1855 in Borneo by A.R. Wallace, and named after the British Rajah Brooke of Sarawak. Wallace named it *Ornithoptera brookeana,* while some authors refer to it as *Troides brookiana.* It is one of the most striking and elegant butterflies in Malaysia, and together with other green-winged Birdwing butterflies, has been bestowed the title 'princes among the butterfly tribes'.

As described by Wallace (*The Malay Archipelago,* 1869), "This beautiful creature has very long and pointed wings, almost resembling a sphinx moth in shape. It is deep velvety black, with a curved band of spots of a brilliant metallic-green colour extending across the wings from tip to tip, each spot being shaped exactly like a small triangular feather, and having very much the effect of a row of the wing coverts of the Mexican trogon laid upon black velvet. The only other marks are a broad neck-collar of vivid

crimson, and a few delicate white touches on the outer margins of the hind wings."

The above account applies to the male butterflies. The markings of the females are, however, quite different and variable. They often have more white on the forewings and wing-tips, and less brilliant colours. In flight, they also present quite a different appearance from that of the male. The male specimens have a wingspan of 16–18 cm, while the females measure 17–19 cm.

Three races or subspecies of Rajah Brooke's Birdwing are present in Malaysia. They are *Trogonoptera brookiana albescens* and *Trogonoptera brookiana mollumar* in Peninsular Malaysia, and *Trogonoptera brookiana trogon* in East Malaysia (the last is also found in Sumatra, Palawan and Natuna Island).

The race *albescens* is rather local in its distribution in Peninsular Malaysia. It is confined to the central states of Perak,

Pahang and Selangor. The male butterflies are not uncommon along the banks of forest streams at low to moderate elevations, and groups of them may settle at moist places along forest paths and river banks. The females, on the other hand, prefer higher elevations, fly higher (often 10 metres up in the flowering trees) and may be still on the wing in the early evening. They only descend to ground level in the early morning.

Like *albescens,* the race *mollumar* is restricted to the swampy forest land in Johore, north-eastern Pahang and Trengganu. Unlike *albescens,* no congregations of the male *mollumar* butterflies have been reported. The female butterfly is not very dissimilar from the male, and both sexes visit flowers. As in *mollumar,* the *trogon* males never congregate to drink at damp places.

Although strictly a jungle species, Rajah Brooke's Birdwing often comes close to inhabited areas. The caterpillars feed on species of *Aristolochia* and the butterfly has been successfully bred in Sumatra.

# *Troides helena* (Linnaeus)

## COMMON BIRDWING

This is a widespread species occurring from Sri Lanka and India to south-east China and through South-east Asia to New Guinea. It is a jungle species but frequents forest clearings and is seen occasionally in rural cultivated areas and urban gardens.

The male butterflies do not drink at wet places along forest paths. They have a wingspan of 13–15 cm. The females are much larger, with a wingspan of 16–18 cm, and have large black spots on the hindwings.

This butterfly has been bred in Malaysia. The caterpillars feed on *Aristolochia*; the usual food plant in Peninsular Malaysia is *Aristolochia tagala*.

The colour pattern of the Common Birdwing is typical of many species of *Troides*. It has been suggested that adult *Troides* butterflies are distasteful to predators and that their yellow-and-black coloration is a warning pattern.

Several other species are somewhat similar to *Troides helena*. Of these, the Malayan Birdwing *Troides amphrysus* (Cramer) is most likely to be encountered. It generally frequents lowland and foothill forests. Another species, the Golden Birdwing *Troides aeacus* (C. & R. Felder) is known to contain poisonous acetylcholine-like substances in its tissues.

*Troides helena* ♀

▲ *Troides amphrysus* ♂ ▶

28

## *Atrophaneura coon* (Fabricius)

COMMON CLUBTAIL

This elegant butterfly has a wingspan of 10–13 cm. It is distributed from Assam and Burma to Thailand, Peninsular Malaysia, Sumatra and Java; it is not present in East Malaysia and other parts of Borneo.

The female butterfly resembles the male, and both have the last few abdominal segments coloured pale pink. They are essentially forest insects. In Peninsular Malaysia, they are confined to the plains throughout the country. In some parts of the country, they may be found flying around *Lantana* blossoms. The caterpillars feed on *Apama tomentosa*.

# *Atrophaneura neptunus* (Guérin-Méneville)

## YELLOW-BODIED CLUBTAIL

This beautiful butterfly is related to the Common Clubtail. The distal half of its abdomen is coloured bright yellow, while the hindwing has a bright carmine subtornal patch.

This species is present in Borneo. It has a wingspan of 10–12 cm. It frequents rather open woods on the plains, but is not common. The food plant of its caterpillar is *Thottea.*

Unlike the Clubtails, other species of *Atrophaneura* are without tails on the hindwing, *e.g.* the Malayan Batwing *A. nox* (Swainson) and *A. sycorax* (Grose Smith) (called *kepala puteh* in Malay because of its creamy white head and prothorax).

*Atrophaneura* butterflies are related to *Troides,* and are often grouped together as the 'Aristolochia Papilios'. They are, however, smaller and have shorter wings. Their bodies or heads always have some kind of red or yellow markings.

# *Pachliopta aristolochiae* (Fabricius)

COMMON ROSE

This striking, red, black and white butterfly bears a general resemblance to the Common Clubtail *(Atrophaneura coon)*, and has been regarded by some authors as a species of *Atrophaneura*. It differs from *A. coon* in having a more robust appearance, broader hindwing and less spatulate tail.

The male and female butterflies are similar, and have a wingspan of 8–11 cm. In Malaysia, they inhabit well-wooded localities throughout the country, but appears to be rather localised. They are also found from Sri Lanka and India to South China and other parts of South-east Asia.

The food plants of the caterpillars include *Aristolochia tagala* and *Apama* and *Thottea* species.

Adult Common Rose is said to be distasteful to most insectivores and exhibit warning coloration. It has at least one mimic—a female form *(romulus)* of *Papilio* *polytes*. The Common Rose, however, differs from *P. polytes* in having a red body.

# *Papilio demoleus* (Linnaeus)

## LIME BUTTERFLY

The Lime Butterfly is also known as the Chequered Swallowtail. It is distributed from north-east Arabia, through India, Sri Lanka, Indo-China and the Lesser Sunda Islands, to New Guinea and northern Australia. It does not occur in the Large Sunda Islands (Sumatra, Java, Borneo), Sulawesi, Moluccas and the Philippines. In Africa and South Arabia, it is replaced by a phenetically identical species called Esper Citrus Swallowtail or Christmas Butterfly (*Papilio demodocus*).

In Malaysia, the Lime Butterfly is found only in the plains of the peninsula. It has a wingspan of 8–10 cm. The two sexes are virtually identical; the female, however, has a large black circular spot above the red spot on the hindwing.

The common name of this butterfly indicates its intimate association with the lime and other citrus plants. The caterpillars, however, are known to feed on several species of legumes. Flowering legumes also provide a source of nectar for the adult butterflies.

Although at one time a very common butterfly in gardens and villages where citrus plants are grown, the Lime Butterfly today does not appear to enjoy the same status as a result of changing environment and the indiscriminate widespread use of pesticides.

# *Papilio demolion* (Cramer)

### BANDED SWALLOWTAIL

As its common name indicates, the Banded Swallowtail has a pale yellow-green band which extends from the apex of the forewing to the mid-dorsum of the hindwing. It has a wingspan of 9–10 cm. The male and female butterflies are similar and are swift in flight.

Although it is found in well-wooded areas at all elevations, the Banded Swallowtail is commoner on the plains in Malaysia. It also occurs in south Burma, Thailand, Sumatra and Java.

## *Papilio nephelus* (Boisduval)

### BLACK AND WHITE HELEN

This is a black butterfly with a large, white to creamy white discal patch on the hindwing. The subspecies *Papilio nephelus sunatus* Corbet also possesses a prominent white macular band on the forewing. It has a wingspan of 11–13 cm.

The Black and White Helen has a swift, restless flight. It frequents forest paths on the plains and in low hills, but is more abundant on the plains.

# *Papilio helenus* (Linnaeus)

RED HELEN

The Red Helen is perhaps the most abundant Papilionid butterfly on the hills. Although present, it is less common on the plains. It flies along jungle paths and roads, and may also come to the banks of forest streams.

It has a wingspan of 11–13 cm. The hindwing has a discal patch consisting of three large white or pale yellow spots, and a complete row of red submarginal spots; these red spots are, however, usually not found on the upperside of the male.

The white discal patch on the hindwing is conspicuous in flight, but is covered by the forewings when the butterfly is at rest. It has been suggested that this is an example of 'flash coloration'. The sudden display of the white patch when the butterfly takes off may momentarily disconcert an enemy.

There are a number of other Papilionid butterflies with black and white coloration. Of these, the Great Helen *Papilio iswara* White is similar to the Red Helen in appearance but is larger, with a wingspan of 13–15 cm. It prefers rather open forest areas in the vicinity of streams. Like the Red Helen, it appears to be commoner on the hills than on the plains.

Another species, *Papilio fuscus* Goeze has a distinctive white patch on the hindwing. It inhabits lowland forest and appears to be uncommon. Like many other butterflies, it may be found drinking at moist places such as river banks.

*Papilio fuscus*

*Papilio helenus*

## *Papilio polytes* (Linnaeus)

COMMON MORMON

The common name of this butterfly is derived from the fact that the female is polymorphic. There are three female colour forms of which two are found in Malaysia.

Male Common Mormon is black above, with a creamy white, oblique band extending from the apex of the forewing to the middle of the inner margin of the hindwing. It is swifter in flight than the female. Of the female butterflies, form *cyrus* is similar to the male whereas form *romulus* is a mimic of *Pachliopta aristolochiae* but with entirely black body. The female form *romulus* imitates the flight as well as the appearance of the poisonous model. The third female colour form resembles *Pachliopta hector* and appears to be confined to Sri Lanka.

This butterfly has a wingspan of 9–10 cm. It is found only on the plains and has become adapted to an urban life. It is common in citrus growing areas but not so in forest land. Its life history is similar to that of *Papilio demoleus* and their caterpillars are almost indistinguishable. In addition to citrus plants, the caterpillars also feed on wild species of Rutaceae.

# *Papilio memnon* (Linnaeus)

## GREAT MORMON

The Great Mormon has a large and striking appearance. Its wings are 12–15 cm in expanse. The males are more easily seen than the females although both sexes may be equally abundant. They are found in gardens, open country and forests; the females are, however, normally confined to the forest.

The male butterfly has a black upper surface streaked with metallic blue, and a tailless hindwing with scalloped edges. It has been suggested to mimick the males of *Atrophaneura* species such as *A. nox* and *A. varuna*.

Female Great Mormon occurs in a great variety of forms. They vary so much that they were once regarded as distinct species. These female colour forms may be tailless like the male or they may possess spoon-shaped tails on the hindwings.

Of the tailless forms, *butlerianus* and *esperi* are more usually encountered. The form *butlerianus* resembles the female

*Papilio memnon*

*Atrophaneura varuna,* while form *esperi* mimicks female *Atrophaneura nox.* Both these female forms differ from the male in having black abdomen.

The tailed form *distantianus* is commonest in central-north Peninsular Malaysia. It is a good copy of *Atrophaneura coon* but with its abdomen marked with yellowish buff.

In East Malaysia (and other parts of Borneo), there occur other female forms which mimick the females of *Troides helena* and *Troides amphrysus;* these are form *venusia* and form *anura* respectively. Furthermore, the Bornean *acheron* (*Papilio acheron* Grose Smith) looks like a miniature Great Mormon, the female being of the *esperi* type. The specific status of *acheron* is, however, uncertain.

*Papilio acheron*

41

# *Graphium sarpedon* (Linnaeus)

COMMON BLUEBOTTLE

This butterfly is easily recognised by the simple pale bluish green macular band running from the apex of the forewing to the inner margin of the hindwing. It is also referred to as the Blue Triangle in other countries.

The male and female butterflies are similar except for the scent fold on the hindwing of the male. They are swift in flight and have a wingspan of 8–9 cm. They are common in forested areas, particularly at lower altitudes. The males may also congregate to drink at moist spots on forest roads and river banks.

The caterpillars feed on various species of Lauraceae. In Australia, they may be a minor pest of Camphor laurel *(Cinnamomum)*.

# *Graphium eurypylus* (Linnaeus)

GREAT JAY

This fast flying butterfly is also known as the Pale Green Triangle in some countries. It has a wingspan of 7–9 cm. The wings flutter rapidly even when the butterfly alights on flowers or other surfaces. This confers the Great Jay to be described as a 'nervous' butterfly.

The Great Jay comes readily to *Lantana* flowers and moist places. Its caterpillar has been reported in some countries to be a minor pest of cultivated custard apple.

There are a number of other *Graphium* butterflies which resemble the Great Jay. Two common species are *Graphium doson* (C. & R. Felder) and *Graphium evemon* (Boisduval). The Great Jay is characterised by the presence of a red spot on the dark costal bar that is joined to the dark basal band. This red spot is absent in the Common Jay *Graphium doson* and *Graphium evemon*. *Graphium doson* is further characterised by its costal bar being separate from all other black markings.

*Graphium evemon*

*Graphium eurypylus.*

43

# *Graphium agamemnon* (Linnaeus)

## TAILED JAY

This butterfly has a characteristic speckled appearance. It has a stumpy tail on the hindwing, and a wingspan of 8.5–10 cm. It is widely distributed in open country at low elevations. The males are often seen at *Lantana* flowers. Like other *Graphium* butterflies the adult butterfly may drink at moist places and the caterpillar feeds on various species of Annonaceae, including the cultivated custard apple and soursop.

The Great Jay is also commonly known as the Green-spotted Triangle and Tailed Green Jay.

# *Pathysa antiphates* (Cramer)

FIVEBAR SWORDTAIL

As its common name indicates, this butterfly has a very long, slender and tapering tail on the hindwing, and five incomplete black bands on the forewing. It has a wingspan of 8–9.5 cm.

The Fivebar Swordtail is a lowland forest butterfly. It is a swift flier and may be mistaken to be a Pierid butterfly. The males may sometimes be seen congregated at moist places. They, and also males of other species of Papilionidae and Pieridae, are attracted by dead Fivebar Swordtail males on the roadside. The females are rarely encountered.

This butterfly was previously regarded as a species of the genus *Graphium*. Like the *Graphium* butterflies, the Fivebar Swordtail caterpillar feeds on Annonaceae.

## *Paranticopsis delessertii* (Guérin-Méneville)

MALAYAN ZEBRA

In addition to various markings, this butterfly has a characteristic row of distinct, dark submarginal spots and a yellow spot on the hindwing. Both sexes are similar, but the yellow spot is paler and rather obscure in the female.

The Malayan Zebra inhabits well-wooded country at all elevations. The male butterflies may congregate on wet mud and at the sides of forest streams. On the other hand, the female appears to be exceedingly rare. It resembles *Ideopsis gaura* in its colour pattern and its slow fluttering flight.

# *Paranticopsis ramaceus* (Westwood)

PENDLEBURY'S ZEBRA

This is an uncommon forest butterfly. Elsewhere it is also popularly known as the Obscure Zebra. Both sexes appear to be indifferent mimics, the male of *Parantica* or *Radena,* the female of *Euploea.*

The Pendlebury's Zebra occurs in the same vicinity as the Malayan Zebra. The male butterflies also visit moist places such as the sides of forest streams. The female is rarely encountered.

# *Lamproptera meges* (Zinken)

## GREEN DRAGONTAIL

The Dragontail has a unique appearance, with transparent wings and enormously long, drooping tails. The Green Dragontail derives its name from the green band on its wings. It has a wingspan of 4–5.5 cm, and the tails may be 4 cm in length. The sexes are similar. The caterpillar resembles that of a *Papilio*.

This is a forest butterfly found in open places, especially near running water. It is not common and is always found singly. Its flight resembles that of a dragonfly. Even while probing for nectar, it does not settle on the flower but hovers with fast quivering wings. In addition to visiting flowers, it is often found drinking at moist places.

# *Lamproptera curius* (Fabricius)

WHITE DRAGONTAIL

This butterfly resembles the Green Dragontail but has a creamy white instead of green band on the wings. It has a wingspan of 4–5 cm. Like the Green Dragontail, it resembles the dragonfly in flight and inhabits open jungle country at all usual elevations.

The White Dragontail is rarer than the Green Dragontail. It is more often found on the hills, particularly at moist places.

# Family Pieridae

**M**OST species in this family of worldwide occurence are white or yellow or orange in colour, hence the common name White, Yellow and Sulphur butterflies. In many of the white species, the underside of the hindwing is brightly coloured.

Unlike many of the most brilliant butterflies in which the colours are produced by the effect known as 'structural coloration', the colours in the Pieridae are due to chemical pigments (called pterines) produced by the insect and deposited in the scales of its wings during its period of development. The white colour is also due to a form of pterine (called leucopterine), which is chemically similar to uric acid.

None of the Pierid butterflies possess 'tails'. Usually, in the white species, the females are dark-dusted above, and in the yellow species, the females may be paler or even white. The male butterflies often congregate in large numbers at roadside puddles in bright sunshine, or at pools or muddy banks of rivers and streams. On the other hand, the female butterflies prefer the forest shade.

*Eurema* Butterfly

Occasionally, certain species are found in very large numbers and show migratory tendencies. In Peninsular Malaysia, some members of *Appias*, *Catopsilia* and *Delias* have been reported to form migratory swarms.

Like the Swallowtail butterflies, all six legs in the White and Yellow butterflies are functional. Similarly, all Pierids pupate like the Papilionids; the pupae are long, pointed at both ends.

The caterpillars are generally green (brown in *Delias*), cylindrical and smooth, but sometimes with short hairs. Their food plants are chiefly of the families Capparidaceae, Fabaceae, Loranthaceae and Rhamnaceae. In temperate countries some species are pests, particularly of various Cruciferae (*e.g.* cabbages).

*Appias lyncida*

51

# *Delias hyparete* (Linnaeus)

PAINTED JEZEBEL

The Painted Jezebel occurs at all elevations, but is most common at lower altitudes. It frequents open woods, bush and not uncommonly also the gardens. It flies all day and even at dusk.

The sexes are similar, with the female being more dusted with black. They have a wingspan of 7–8 cm. Their brightly coloured underside serves as a warning pattern to predatory animals. Their weak flight further advertises their unpleasant taste.

# *Leptosia nina* (Fabricius)

PSYCHE BUTTERFLY

This is a rather small and fragile white butterfly with a wingspan of 3.5–5 cm. It is the only species of *Leptosia* found in the Oriental Region. Its rather rounded wings have a small black patch at the apex of the forewing. The underside is faintly streaked with green.

The sexes are alike in appearance. They are found in open spaces in the forest at lower elevations. They are feeble in flight and seldom fly high above ground level.

The specific status of this butterfly is in doubt. It has been suggested that it may belong to *L. alcesta* (Cramer) of Africa.

# *Prioneris philonome* (Boisduval)

RED-SPOT SAWTOOTH

This is a large and robust butterfly, with a wingspan of 8–9 cm. The hindwing beneath has a small red basal spot while the basal two-thirds are yellow. The female butterfly appears to be much rarer than the male.

The Red-spot Sawtooth is essentially a forest butterfly. It occurs at all elevations and frequents wayside water seepages in company with other Pierids. It is somewhat similar to *Delias hyparete* in appearance, but it is doubtful whether the resemblance has any mimetic significance.

Two other Malaysian *Prioneris* species are *P. cornelia* and *P. thestylis*.

# *Cepora iudith* (Fabricius)

ORANGE GULL

This butterfly is easily recognised by the bright yellow-orange colour on the tornal half of the upperside of the hindwing.

It is widely distributed on the plains and may be seen drinking on the banks of forest streams and at damp places on jungle paths.

# *Appias lyncida* (Cramer)

CHOCOLATE ALBATROSS

The common name of this butterfly refers to the chocolate wing borders on the underside of the otherwise rich lemon-yellow hindwings. The male is white above, with dentate black border; the female, however, may be almost black with a few broad, whitish streaks. The wings are 5.5–7 cm in expanse.

This butterfly occurs in forest and secondary growth at all elevations, but is commonest on the plains. The males may congregate to drink at damp places on the roadside and along the banks of streams. The females appear to be rarer and are usually found flying among forest undergrowth.

# *Appias libythea* (Fabricius)

STRIPED ALBATROSS

In the male butterfly, the underside of the wings is white with dark veins, hence the common name Striped Albatross or Small Black-veined Albatross. It is, however, yellow dusted in the female. The wings are 5–5.6 cm in expanse.

This is one of the commonest garden and roadside butterflies in Peninsular Malaysia, being established here only in the last 25 years.

# *Appias nero* (Fabricius)

## ORANGE ALBATROSS

This widespread butterfly is probably unique in being the only all-orange coloured butterfly. It is orange or deep red-orange above and yellowish orange beneath. The male has blackened veins on the upperside, while the female has a black border to the wing margins and a short black band on the forewings. The wings are 6.5–8 cm in expanse.

The male butterflies frequent forest paths in the lowlands. They may be found in large numbers at puddles and the banks of forest streams. The females are usually found singly at flowers and prefer higher elevations.

# *Hebomoia glaucippe* (Linnaeus)

GREAT ORANGE TIP

This is the largest Pierid butterfly in Malaysia and the rest of Asia, with a wingspan of 8–10 cm. The wings above are white with a prominent orange-red apical patch outlined with black on the forewing. In the female, there occurs also a row of dark spots along the wing margin. The under surface of the hindwing and the apex of the forewing are mottled brown in colour, giving the butterfly a very leaf-like appearance.

The Great Orange Tip prefers the plains but is occasionally found in the hills. It has a strong flight. The males often visit moist spots and river banks.

## *Catopsilia pyranthe* (Linnaeus)

MOTTLED EMIGRANT

This is the commonest and most widespread species of *Catopsilia* in Malaysia. It is found in the neighbourhood of gardens and villages on the plains.

The upperside of the wings is pale greenish white in colour, while the under surface has a mottled appearance. The wings are 5–7 cm in expanse.

## *Catopsilia pomona* (Fabricius)

LEMON EMIGRANT

Two series of colour forms are included under this species. The *'pomona'* forms have red-ringed spots on the underside of both wings, and their antennae are red above. In contrast, the *'crocale'* forms are without silvery spots on the underside while their antennae are black above. The latter forms are regarded by some as constituting a distinct species, *Catopsilia crocale* (Common Emigrant).

This butterfly has a wingspan of 5.5–8 cm. It is abundant in secondary growth and the vicinity of human dwellings on the plains. It is also occasionally found in forest country and at altitudes up to about 900 metres.

The Lemon Emigrant has been reported migrating in this country (in the State of Perak). It is also often found congregating at damp places. Its caterpillars feed especially on *Cassia* plants.

# *Eurema hecabe* (Linnaeus)

COMMON GRASS YELLOW

This is the commonest Grass Yellow in Malaysia, and the commonest butterfly in the eastern tropics. It is most abundant on the plains, but also not uncommon on the mountains, up to about 1515 metres. Often, it may be found congregating at damp places on forest paths and sand banks along rivers and streams.

The Common Grass Yellow has irregular ring spots on the underside of both wings. It is, however, so highly variable in size (4–5 cm wingspan), colour and markings that no two specimens may be alike.

There are a number of other species of *Eurema* which are rather similar to *E.*

*hecabe*. Of these, the Chocolate Grass Yellow *Eurema sari* (Horsfield) is probably the most plentiful after the Common Grass Yellow. It is easily recognised by the entirely darkened reddish brown apical spot on the forewing beneath. Furthermore, it has only a single cell spot on the underside of the forewing. The Scarce Grass Yellow *Eurema lacteola* (Distant) also has only one cell spot on the forewing. Its apical patch on the underside of the forewing is, however, reduced to a few diffuse spots. It appears to prefer the hills.

The underside of the forewing in the Three-spot Grass Yellow *Eurema blanda* (Boisduval) has three cell spots and a ring-spot at end-cell. It prefers low elevations.

*Eurema hecabe*

▲ *Eurema sari*
◄ *Eurema blanda*
▼ *Eurema lacteola*

# Family Danaidae

MEMBERS of this family are commonly referred to as the milkweed butterflies or Tigers and Crows. They are considered to be the most highly developed of all butterflies. Although traditionally given the status of a Family, some specialists regard them as belonging to a subfamily (Danainae) of the Nymphalidae.

The colouring and type of markings are remarkably conservative in the Danaidae, being mostly yellow-brown, white and black, and blue or greenish blue and black. Nonetheless, many Danaid butterflies serve as models for mimetic butterflies of other families (*e.g.* certain species of Papilionidae, Pieridae, Satyridae and Nymphalidae).

The wings of all Danaid butterflies are extremely resistent to injury. The adult butterflies are also extremely tough and very hard to kill. While most butterflies can easily be killed by pinching the thorax, it is almost impossible to kill a Danaid butterfly in this way. One account states that "... Many a Danaid butterfly, firmly pinched or otherwise killed, and papered by the entomologist, has later, when the paper has been unfolded for inspection, scrambled to its four feet, spread its wings and disappeared through the open window." Another account narrates that "Birds catch them, peck them, and then realising their mistake, release them, and the insect almost always flies away unharmed."

Members of the Danaidae are sun-loving butterflies; they prefer open but sheltered localities, and fly in a leisurely manner. Many of the species are common and the males of many species are gregarious.

The forelegs of Danaid butterflies are imperfect and are useless for walking. All the male butterflies also carry, at the end of the abdomen, a pair of extrusible feathery brushes called hair-pencils. These hair-pencils are brought into use during courtship to brush the scent from a patch of scent scales on the hindwing. They may also be extruded when the butterfly is alarmed. The odour emitted by these hair-pencils is rather strong and pungent.

Danaid caterpillars are usually conspicuously coloured and gregarious. They are generally smooth and cylindrical, with parallel rows of black, white or yellow stripes, and 2–4 pairs of fleshy filamentous tubercles. Their food plants are almost exclusively members of the Asclepiadaceae and Apocynaceae, some of which are poisonous to animals.

The caterpillars feeding on poisonous food plants derive a two-fold benefit. As these poisonous plants are avoided by grazing animals, the caterpillars encounter the minimum risk of being accidentally eaten or otherwise destroyed. Secondly as the ingested plant toxin is stored in the haemolymph (or 'blood') of the insect, it would remain in the subsequent life-stages (chrysalis and adult).

The plant toxin is a heart poison or 'cardenolide'. It also acts on the stomach, so a bird swallowing the butterfly generally vomits it up after 10–15 minutes. Because of the poisonous nature of their body juices, these Danaid butterflies are left alone by birds and other natural predators. It has even been reported that in collections of butterflies ravaged by pests, the Danaidae is always the last to be attacked.

Both the caterpillars and the adult butterflies advertise their distasteful and poisonous nature by 'warning coloration'.

Instead of concealing them, their colours make them conspicuous, so predators quickly learn to recognise and avoid them. In addition, some species also feign death when handled by Man.

The pupae are smooth and bulbous-looking, often brightly coloured with metallic glitter. They are suspended by the tail, head downwards.

▲ Danaid pupa

◄ Danaid caterpillar

▼ *Tirumala septentrionis*

# *Danaus chrysippus* (Linnaeus)

PLAIN TIGER

Two forms of Plain Tiger are found in Malaysia—the hindwing of form *chrysippus* is fulvous orange as in the forewing, whereas it is much paler in form *alcippoides*. They are found only in cultivated and suburban areas, and are confined to the plains.

This butterfly is known in other parts of the world as African Monarch, Lesser Wanderer, and Golden Danaid. The female colour forms are mimicked by the females of *Elymnias hypermnestra* and *Hypolimnas misippus*.

# *Danaus genutia* (Cramer)

COMMON TIGER

As in the Plain Tiger, there are two forms of *Danaus genutia*—form *genutia* has the hindwing coloured like the forewing, whereas the hindwing of the other form is white with the border tinged with orange. The veins are strongly marked with black.

This butterfly is confined to the plains and occurs in secondary growth surrounded by primary forest.

The Common Tiger occurs from Sri Lanka and India to China, and through South-east Asia to Queensland.

In Peninsular Malaysia, it appears that until recently the predominant form is unicolorous. It has since been replaced by the form with white hindwings.

The caterpillar of the Common Tiger has only been reported to feed on *Raphistemma pulchellum*. It has pale bluish white and black bands, and white and yellow spots. There are three pairs of black-tipped, crimson filaments.

The pupa is barrel-shaped. It is pale lustrous green in colour, with black and metallic gold and silver markings.

# *Danaus melanippus* (Cramer)

WHITE/BLACK-VEINED TIGER

This butterfly is very similar to *Danaus genutia* but the ground colour of the hindwing is entirely white and without orange colour as in *D. genutia*. It is more abundant than *D. genutia* and is very common everywhere on the plains except thick forest.

As in *Danaus chrysippus* and *D. genutia*, *D. melanippus* is mimicked by the females of *Elymnias hypermnestra* and *Hypolimnas misippus*.

# *Tirumala septentrionis* (Butler)

DARK BLUE TIGER

This butterfly was previously regarded as a subspecies of *Tirumala hamata* (or *Danaus hamata* in earlier literature). It is more related to *Danaus* than to the similarly marked *Radena*.

The wings are black with blue markings; those on the forewing are narrow and elliptical. The males have a large brand on the hindwing, which protrudes prominently on the underside as a semi-circular flap.

*Tirumala septentrionis* inhabits forested areas at all elevations. It is found together with *Danaus* and *Radena* species.

# *Parantica melaneus* (Cramer)

CHOCOLATE TIGER

This and other species of *Parantica* were previously included as members of the genus *Danaus*.

Its wings are predominantly bluish grey. The underside is lighter, with a dark chocolate brown border on the hindwing. Its abdomen is yellowish brown in colour.

The Chocolate Tiger is a forest butterfly, common at higher elevations. The males are said to emit the strongest scent of all Malaysian Danaidae.

## *Parantica sita* (Kollar)

CHESTNUT TIGER

The Chestnut Tiger is rather similar to *Parantica melaneus* in appearance but larger, hence it is also commonly known as Large Chocolate Tiger. It differs from *P. melaneus* in that the veins and the broad distal border on the hindwing are a rich reddish brown, and the abdomen is dark blackish brown.

Unlike *P. melaneus,* the Chestnut Tiger occurs exclusively on the hills. In the males, the scent scales on the hindwing are indicated by blackening on the reddish-brown border.

The Chestnut Tiger is not as common as the Chocolate Tiger. It is not found in East Malaysia and other areas south of Peninsular Malaysia.

## *Parantica aspasia* (Fabricius)

YELLOW GLASSY TIGER

The colour pattern of this species separates it from other Danaid butterflies. Its wing bases are yellow, that on the hindwing covering about half of the wing surface. As in other *Parantica,* the forewings are predominantly bluish grey with black markings.

This butterfly is found in forested areas at all elevations. It is mimicked by the female of the Pierid butterfly *Pareronia valeria* (The Wanderer) which resembles it closely in appearance and flight.

The caterpillar is velvety black in colour, with yellow spots and numerous white dots, and grey to black filaments. Its food plant is not exactly known.

70

# *Radena vulgaris* (Butler)

BLUE GLASSY TIGER

This butterfly closely resembles the Dark Glassy Tiger *Parantica agleoides* (C. &. R. Felder) but may be easily distinguished by the forewing cell; the pale cell streak in *R. vulgaris* is diagonally divided by a black bar, while that of *P. agleoides* has only a thin longitudinal black line.

The Blue Glassy Tiger is very common at all elevations. It has a very similar looking relative, *Radena similis* (Linnaeus) which is larger and has wider markings. Elsewhere, *R. similis* is commonly referred to as the Blue Glassy Tiger.

# *Ideopsis gaura* (Horsfield)

## SMALLER WOOD NYMPH

The ground colour in this butterfly is smoky grey. Its large black spots are arranged much as in the Tree Nymph *Idea lynceus* (Drury). The male has darker ground colour and narrower wings than the female.

This is essentially a forest butterfly, occurring at all elevations but less frequently on the plains. It has a slow undulating flight, and may fly in more open country.

The Lesser Wood Nymph is mimicked by the females of the Papilionid *Paranticopsis delessertii*, the Satyrid *Elymnias kuenstleri*, and the Zygaenid moth *Cyclosia pieridoides*.

## *Euploea crameri* Lucas

SPOTTED BLACK CROW

This butterfly has a distinctive group of 4 large spots at the apex of the forewing. The wings are blackish brown above, with only marginal and submarginal white spots.

In Peninsular Malaysia, it is not uncommon in secondary growth in Langkawi Islands and on the east coast, but appears to be rare elsewhere in the Peninsula.

The male butterfly does not have a brand on its upperside forewing. The female butterfly is paler than the male in colour.

A similar-looking species, the Common Indian Crow *Euploea core* (Cramer) appears to be absent in East Malaysia.

## *Euploea doubledayi* C. & R. Felder

LARGER STRIPED BLACK CROW

In Malaysia this butterfly is found only in the northern half of the Peninsula. It is very similar to the Striped Black Crow *Euploea eyndhovii* C. & R. Felder but is larger. The hindwing has a characteristic series of white marginal spots and a corresponding row of elongate, white submarginal streaks.

This butterfly prefers rather open forest country at all usual elevations.

The male butterfly has a dark brand on its upperside forewing, and a blackened speculum on the upperside hindwing. The female butterfly is paler than the male butterfly.

Another similar-looking species is *Euploea algea* (Godart). The hindwing speculum in the male of this species is not blackened.

# *Euploea mulciber* (Cramer)

STRIPED BLUE CROW

This is the commonest species of *Euploea* in Malaysia. It is a forest butterfly, but often seen in clearings and along forest roads both on the plains and the hills.

Male and female Striped Blue Crows differ in their colour patterns. The forewing in the male is predominantly bright blue with white spots in the distal half of the wing, whereas the female is dark brown with white spots on the blue-shot distal half. In addition, the hindwing in the female has narrow white streaks arranged in the manner of *Radena* species.

Both sexes of *Euploea mulciber* are mimicked by the respective sexes of the Satyrid *Elymnias casiphone*. The male is also mimicked by the Papilionid *Chilasa paradoxa* f. *aenigina* and the Zygaenid moth *Cyclosia midamia*.

Male *Euploea mulciber*

Female *Euploea mulciber*

# *Euploea diocletianus* (Fabricius)

## MAGPIE CROW

The markings on the wings of this butterfly are distinctive, although the two sexes differ in the colour pattern. In the male the ground colour is a rich velvety bluish black, while the female is browner and has more extensive white areas on both wings. The abdominal scent brushes of the male are said to disseminate a strong but pleasant, vanilla-like scent, which is seductive to the female *E. diocletianus*.

Male Magpie Crows are common everywhere (along forest roads, at wet places, banks of streams, quarries, *etc*) on the plains as well as the hills. The females appear to be less common and prefer higher altitudes.

Both sexes of Magpie Crow are mimicked by the respective sexes of the Papilionid *Chilasa paradoxa* f. *aegialus*. In addition, the male Magpie Crow is mimicked by the Satyrid *Elymnias penanga* ♀-f. *penanga* and the Nymphalid *Euripus nyctelius* ♀-f. *isina*, while the female Magpie Crow is mimicked by the female of *Elymnias harterti* and *Euripus nyctelius* ♀-f. *euploeoides*.

# Family Satyridae

**M**EMBERS of this family of butterflies (as conceived here) belong to
two distinct but closely related
groups, the Satyrs and Browns (Subfamily
Satyrinae) and the Amathusiids (Subfamily
Amathusiinae). These two groups were
traditionally regarded as two separate
families, Satyridae and Amathusiidae. Some
specialists also regard them as subfamilies
of the greater family Nymphalidae. The
Satyrid butterflies, however, differ from the
Nymphalids in habit; for instance they shun
sunshine and prefer the shade, rarely visit
flowers, and are crepuscular, flying at early
morning and late afternoon or evening.
Furthermore, the Satyrid caterpillars feed
on monocotyledonous plants (grasses,
palms and bamboos), while the Nymphalid
caterpillars feed on dicotyledons.

The Satyrines and Amathusiids may be
distinguished by their wing venation.
Nonetheless, the adult Amathusiids are
much like large Satyrines except that many
of them bear brilliant metallic blue patches.
Their caterpillars are also very similar except
that the Amathusiid caterpillars are often
covered with long tufts of hair.

Like the Nymphalids, the forelegs of
Satyrid butterflies are poorly developed and
brush-like and are not used for walking.

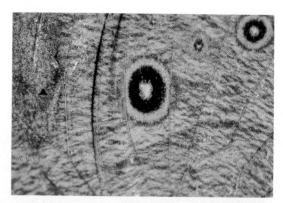

Eyespot of *Melanitis leda*

Malayan Owl *Neorina lowii*

Unlike other butterflies, adult Satyrids are very prone to losing their scales when handled.

Satyrid butterflies are seldom prominent and are usually dull-coloured. They generally fly close to the ground and near shelter. Although their flights are seldom rapid (in fact weak and erratic in Satyrs and Browns), they are expert at dodging into cover and hiding when alarmed. Their sombre colouring and crepuscular habits protect them reasonably well from predators.

Most Satyrid butterflies are generally some shade of brown in colour, and almost invariably with a number of round, ringed eye-spots on the underside of the wings. In many species the underside pattern is cryptic. Some of the species add to the effect of their cryptic (concealing) patterns by leaning towards the sun when at rest and thus reducing their shadows, which might otherwise be conspicuous.

*Amathusia gunneryi*

# *Melanitis leda* (Linnaeus)

## COMMON EVENING BROWN

This is a very variable butterfly. The upperside is dark brown, with a large black subapical patch on the forewing bearing two white spots and inwardly shaded with orange. The underside is buff or grey, with fine dark brown transverse striations. There may be present on both wings a submarginal series of white-centred, yellow-ringed black eyespots.

This is a shade-loving butterfly which is largely confined to the plains. As its caterpillar feeds on rice, it is usually common where padi is cultivated. It usually flies only at dawn and shortly after dusk. It is well-camouflaged when it settles among dead leaves on the forest floor.

# *Elymnias hypermnestra* (Linnaeus)

## COMMON PALMFLY

This is the commonest and most widespread representative of *Elymnias* butterflies. It is a weak flier, fluttering around in the shade and generally avoiding bright sunshine.

In the male, the upperside of the forewing is bluish black with a series of blue submarginal spots. The underside is a rich mottled brown, with a 'thumb print' paler shade at the apex of the forewing and a prominent white spot on the margin of the hindwing.

There occurs at least two female forms. The blue ♀-form, which is found in most parts of Malaysia, is similar to the male but lighter in colour and has a few whitish submarginal spots on the upperside of the hindwing. On the other hand, the orange ♀-form, which is found in Kedah and Langkawi Islands resembles *Danaus chrysippus* and *D. genutia;* this ♀-form even flies in bright sunshine. Hybrids between these two forms with intermediate pattern are found in south Kedah and Penang.

# *Lethe chandica* (Moore)

## ANGLED RED FORESTER

This butterfly has a very irregular discal line on the underside of both wings. The male has an extensive black patch in the discal area on the upperside of the forewing.

The ground colour of this butterfly appears to be variable. Although present in lowland forests, it occurs most often at moderate elevations in the hills.

The caterpillar is green in colour. It feeds on bamboo.

Two other common species are *Lethe europa* (Fabricius) and *Lethe mekara* (Moore). The Bamboo Tree-Brown (*Lethe europa*) is often found near human habitations where bamboo is present. It is most frequently encountered during the rainy season. Being active at dawn and dusk, it is not easily encountered during the daytime.

*Lethe mekara* is a more ornate butterfly than *L. europa*. It has been found to feed on animal dropping.

Two other very rare mountain species are *Lethe vindhya* (C. & R. Felder) and *Lethe sinorax* (Hewitson). Two further mountain species, *Lethe darena* C. & R. Felder and *Lethe delila* Staudinger, are found in Borneo.

---

# *Lethe verma* (Kollar)

## STRAIGHT-BANDED TREEBROWN

This butterfly has a quadrate forewing bearing a broad white subapical band in both sexes. There are no apical spots on the upperside of the forewing; such spots are present in a similar-looking species, the Banded Treebrown *Lethe confusa* Aurivillius.

In Malaysia, this butterfly appears to be restricted to Cameron Highlands. Its endemic nature calls for detailed studies concerning its conspecific status with that found in other countries.

# *Neorina lowii* (Doubleday)

MALAYAN OWL

This is one of the largest Satyrid butterflies. Its coloration is distinctive—dark blackish brown above, with a large white patch at the tornus of the forewing and the apex of the hindwing. A large subapical eyespot is present on the forewing, while a similar smaller spot occurs in the tornal area of the hindwing. The underside of the wings is paler than the upperside, and has an additional eyespot in the apical area of the hindwing.

The Malayan Owl is not a common species. It lives in dense lowland forest, and has a similar distribution as *Trogonoptera brookiana*.

This butterfly may feed on rotten fruits on the jungle floor. Its early stages are unknown.

A fossil butterfly *(Neorinopsis sepulta)* discovered in Oligocene deposits at Aix-en Provence, France, closely resembles the Malayan Owl.

# *Mycalesis fusca* (C. & R. Felder)

MALAYAN BUSH BROWN

The underside of this forest butterfly is ochreous brown with two reddish brown longitudinal stripes on both wings. The submarginal spots are small, and are not ringed with white. The female is larger than the male, and has more rounded forewings and a distinctly paler underside.

Two related species—the Tawny Bush Brown *Mycalesis anapita* Moore and *M. patiana* Eliot—have a broad black forewing border on the brownish orange upperside.

▲ *Mycalesis patiana*

▼ *Mycalesis fusca* ▶

## *Mycalesis janardana* Moore

COMMON BUSH BROWN

This butterfly is quite distinctive. Its underside is pale greyish brown, uniformly stippled, and crossed by a narrow dull-white post-discal stripe. The submarginal eyespots are rather uniform in size.

The Common Bush Brown inhabits the undergrowth of primary and secondary forests at moderate elevations.

The male butterfly has a brand on its upperside hindwing. This brand has two separated hair tufts, as compared to the single hair tuft in other species of *Mycalesis*.

Although not uncommon, the life history of this butterfly appears to be unknown.

## *Mycalesis mineus* (Linnaeus)

DARK BRAND BUSH BROWN

This is the commonest *Mycalesis* butterfly in Malaysia. Its upperside is dark greyish brown, while the underside is paler with a clear-white post-discal stripe and a series of submarginal eyespots. It is a lowland butterfly.

*Mycalesis mineus*

There are a number of other species belonging to the *mineus* group. Of these, *M. intermedia* (Moore) is not found in East Malaysia while *M. horsfieldi* (Moore) is rare.

Another species, the Purple Bush Brown *M. orseis* Hewitson, bears close resemblance to the *mineus* group but is not closely related.

▲ *Mycalesis mineus*

*Mycalesis intermedia* ▶
*Mycalesis horsfieldi* ▶

▼ *Mycalesis orseis*

# *Mycalesis maianeas* Hewitson

## BANDLESS BUSH BROWN

The upperside of this butterfly is dark brown, with the subapical area of the forewing paler in the male, and with a diffuse orange band in the female. The underside is also dark brown with paler apex on the forewing and with irregular markings on both wings.

A related species, the Red Bush Brown *M. oroatis* Hewitson, has reddish brown upperside and the underside has a narrow purplish white post-discal stripe. This butterfly is not present in East Malaysia.

Both the above species inhabit thick forests and are uncommon.

*Mycalesis oroatis*

*Mycalesis maianeas*

# *Orsotriaena medus* (Fabricius)

NIGGER

The underside of this butterfly is distinctive, with two submarginal eyespots on the forewing and three on the hindwing, and a prominent clear white discal line across both wings. The upperside is dark brown and unmarked.

This butterfly is very similar and is related to those of *Mycalesis,* but has smooth eyes. It is very common in shady places on the plains. The caterpillar feeds on grasses, including rice.

# *Erites angularis* Moore

ANGLED CYCLOPS

This butterfly has two characteristic reddish brown stripes and a series of submarginal eyespots on the underside of both wings. Both the inner and outer stripes on the hindwing are sharply angled. The upperside is dull greyish brown.

The Angled Cyclops is feeble in flight, furtive in habit and is confined to thick lowland forest. It does not occur in East Malaysia.

The life history of the Angled Cyclops is unknown.

# *Ragadia makuta* (Horsfield)

STRIPED RINGLET

The underside of this butterfly is striped chocolate brown and light buff, and has a complete series of submarginal eyespots. The upperside is pale brown in colour. It has a feeble fluttering flight and inhabits the undergrowth of primary forest at all usual elevations.

A very similar species is the Zebra Ringlet *Ragadia crisilda* Hewitson, which is found only in hills from about 1220 to 1520 metres and does not occur in East Malaysia. The underside is, however, striped dark brown and white.

*Ragadia makuta*

*Ragadia crisilda*

# *Ypthima pandocus* Moore

## COMMON THREE-RING

This butterfly gets its common name from the three yellow-ringed black submarginal eyespots on the hindwing. It is the larger and commonest *Ypthima* butterfly in Malaysia. It occurs at all elevations, in the forest, in secondary growth, and even in the gardens.

There are a number of other *Ypthima* butterflies which are separated by the number and arrangement of submarginal eyespots on the hindwing. Of these, the Common Four-ring *Y. ceylonica* Hewitson and the Common Five-ring *Y. baldus* (Fabricius) are common at low elevation in primary and secondary growth ( *Y. ceylonica* is, however, not found in East Malaysia).

The Pallid Five-ring *Y. savara* Grose Smith is a rare forest species, while *Y. fasciata* Hewitson with seven small submarginal eyespots is the least abundant of the common species.

In giving these *Ypthima* butterflies their common names, the two spots at the hindwing tornus contained in a single yellow outer ring are counted as one ring.

*Ypthima pandocus*

▲ *Ypthima baldus*

◄ *Ypthima ceylonica*

▲ *Ypthima fasciata*

◄ *Ypthima savara*

# *Faunis canens* Hübner

COMMON FAUN

This is an inconspicuous butterfly inhabiting dense forest at low elevations. It is usually seen close to the ground.

The underside of the wings are deep brown with dark discal lines and a submarginal series of small whitish dots. The upper surface is orange brown and unmarked.

A similar but smaller species is *F. gracilis* (Butler), which differs in having two prominent, white-centred, black eyespots on the underside of the hindwing.

*Faunis gracilis*

*Faunis canens*

# *Melanocyma faunula* (Westwood)

## PALLID FAUN

The underside of this butterfly is distinctive with three dark wavy bands. Otherwise it is similar to *Faunis* in structure. It inhabits thick forests up to about 1515 metres in altitude, and does not occur in East Malaysia.

# *Amathusia phidippus* (Linnaeus)

## PALM KING

This butterfly is very similar to other species of *Amathusia* and positive identification requires examination of the secondary sexual characters of the male. It is the most widespread of *Amathusia* butterflies and is found especially in the vicinity of coconut palm. It is crepuscular in habit and often enters lighted houses.

A very similar species is *A. gunneryi* Corbet & Pendlebury, which was previously regarded as a pale form of *A. phidippus*. Its underside has a washed-out appearance and is glazed with faint markings. This butterfly is confined to localised areas in Peninsular Malaysia.

One of the larger species is *A. schoenbergi* Honrath. In this species the outer edge of the broad reddish brown band on the under surface of the forewing is wavy and deeply indented.

*Amathusia phidippus*

*Amathusia gunneryi*

*Amathusia schoenbergi*

## *Enispe intermedia* Rothschild

RED CALIPH

The upperside of this butterfly is orange brown, heavily marked with black spots and zig-zag lines. The under surface is dull reddish brown with two eyespots on the hindwing and a rather broad median band crossing both wings. This butterfly inhabits both lowland and hill forests.

The male butterfly has a speculum on its underside forewing. The female butterfly is larger than the male, and is paler in colour.

This butterfly is previously known as *Enispe euthymius* (Doubleday). Its life history is unknown.

## *Thauria aliris* (Westwood)

TUFTED JUNGLE KING

This large butterfly has a distinct colour pattern on both wing surfaces. It occurs both on the plains and mountain areas. The adult feeds on rotting jungle fruits.

♂ ▼ ♀ ▶

## *Amathuxidia amythaon*
(Doubleday)

KOH-I-NOOR

The underside of this butterfly is distinctive, being pinkish brown or pinkish blue with prominent dark lines and large eyespots. It inhabits primary forest mainly on the plains. It does not fly much, and even when disturbed, does not fly far. The male is said to exude a pleasant sweet scent which remains for some time after its death.

# Family Nymphalidae

MEMBERS of this family are commonly called brush-footed butterflies because the forelegs in the adults are hairy and brush-like, as are also found in Danaids and Satyrids. Some specialists also regard the Danaid and Satyrid butterflies as members of this family. The male Nymphalid butterflies, unlike the Danaids and Satyrids, however, do not possess special scent brands on the wings.

As in Danaids and Satyrids, the forelegs in adult Nymphalid butterflies are greatly reduced in size and useless for walking; hence the butterflies, when walking or resting, are functionally four-legged. The forelegs, however, serve as sense organs, with the end joints serving as organs of taste. The brushes are also sometimes used in the cleaning of the antennae.

The Nymphalid butterflies have a great fondness for sunshine, and are often seen at flowering plants in the garden and forest, and by the roadside. They have a swift, powerful and well-controlled flight.

Adult Nymphalid butterflies exhibit great variation in size, shape, colouring and habits. Many of them are often brightly coloured, while some are sombrely and

Caterpillars of *Cethosia penthesilea*

*Cethosia hypsea*

cryptically coloured—the most celebrated being those with leaf-like patterns on the under surface such as the Indian Leaf Butterfly (*Kallima paralekta*). Some of them have curiously shaped wings with hooked tips and long, slender tails. A few of them have eye-spot ornamentation, while some species mimic other butterflies of protected, warningly coloured groups (*e.g. Hypolimnas misippus* female is totally different from the male and is a faithful copy of *Danaus chrysippus*).

Sexual dimorphism is quite marked in some Nymphalid species. In a few species the females, or even the males in some instances, may be polymorphic. In areas with distinct seasons, seasonal dimorphism is also known. Furthermore, many species of Nymphalids are either regular migrants (*e.g. Cynthia cardui* L.) or known to take part in migratory movements (*e.g. Precis* species).

The Nymphalid butterflies are made up of a number of subfamilies which may be distinguished easily by the early stages. The caterpillars, though varied, are usually quite spiny, often with branching spines arising from prominent tubercles, and are sometimes ornately horned on the head. The chrysalids also show amazing diversity of form. They are, however, frequently very brightly coloured and ornamented with brilliant metallic flecks. It was from the golden ornamentation which led to the name 'chrysalis' for butterfly pupa (*chrysos* being the Greek word for 'golden'). The name 'Aurelians' (applied in ancient days to people concerned with entomology) was similarly derived, from the Latin *aureus* for 'golden'.

Related to the Nymphalid groups of butterflies are the members of the very small family Libytheidae, known commonly as 'snout or beak butterflies' because of their extraordinarily long palpi which project in front like a long straight beak. Unlike the Nymphalids, the forelegs are imperfect only in the male but functionally perfect in the female. The wings are angulate and patterned with darker and lighter shades of brown.

*Terinos atlita*

## *Ariadne ariadne* (Linnaeus)

ANGLED CASTOR

This butterfly has a characteristic pose when at rest. The upperside of its wings is rich reddish brown with 5 or 6 narrow, black, rather wavy transverse lines. The duller under surface is also crossed by some irregular dark bands. There is a prominent white subapical streak on the forewing.

The Angled Castor is usually found in forest clearings or in open spaces along jungle paths at low elevations.

## *Phalanta alcippe* (Stoll)

SMALL LEOPARD

This is a common butterfly in forest clearings on the plains. Its wings are rich orange brown, ornamented with black spots and streaks. Both wings are bordered with black, and the upperside is tinged with pinkish purple.

## *Vagrans egista* (Cramer)

VAGRANT

This butterfly is orange brown with brownish black margins, spots and patches on both wings. Its hindwing has a short tail. It is found in clearings, quarries and forest edges, and prefers the hills to the plains.

## *Cirrochroa orissa* C. & R. Felder

BANDED YEOMAN

This is the commonest species of *Cirrochroa* in Malaysia. It frequents forest edges and clearings at all suitable elevations. The upperside of its forewing is distinctive, being broadly bordered with black at the apex, and with a very broad yellow oblique post-discal band.

## *Cirrochroa emalea* (Guérin-Méneville)

MALAY YEOMAN

The upper surface of this butterfly is coloured orange brown, with a black margin on the apex of the forewing and black wavy marginal and submarginal lines on both wings. It is found along forest edge at all elevations, and has been reported to take part in migratory movement.

## *Paduca fasciata* (C. & R. Felder)

BRANDED YEOMAN

This butterfly is greyish brown, with a yellow discal band and yellow post-discal and submarginal fasciae on both wings. It has a feeble flight and frequents secluded forest paths on the plains and up to about 600 metres in altitude.

# *Vindula dejone* (Erichson)

CRUISER

The two sexes of this butterfly have different colours on the wings; the male is orange brown while the female is bluish green or dark greenish brown. Both sexes are, however, similarly marked— a band of a lighter colour on both wings, dark patterning along the wing margins, and eyespots on the hindwing. The hindwing has a short tail.

This butterfly is commonest on the plains, where it frequents open country as well as forest and is strongly attracted by *Lantana* flowers. It is replaced in the hills by a very similar but larger species, *V. erota* (Fabricius).

▼ *Vindula dejone* ▶

◀*Vindula erota* ♀        *Vindula erota* ♂ ▲ ▼

# *Cethosia hypsea* Doubleday

MALAY LACEWING

The common name for this and other related butterflies is derived from the lacewing pattern of the underside of their wings. These Lacewing butterflies are coloured bright orange-red and black above, and orange-red richly variegated with white and black beneath. The outer margins of both wings are toothed.

*Cethosia hypsea* is the commonest Lacewing butterfly in Malaysia, and is characterised by a white subapical band on the forewing. A very similar species is the Plain Lacewing *C. penthesilea* (Cramer), which has a narrow white submarginal band on the underside of its wings. A third species, the Red Lacewing *C. biblis* (Drury), does not possess a white subapical band on the forewing but has instead a series of white spots and lunules.

Both *C. hypsea* and *C. penthesilea* are fairly common at flowering plants on forest roads at low to moderate elevations, while *C. biblis* is largely confined to the hills. These butterflies emit an unpleasant odour when squeezed.

*Cethosia hypsea* (ventral view)

*Cethosia hypsea* (dorsal view)

▲ *Cethosia penthesilea* (dorsal view)

▼ *Cethosia penthesilea* (ventral view)

# *Precis iphita* (Cramer)

CHOCOLATE PANSY

The upper surface of the wings in this butterfly is brown with indistinct darker bands, and a row of minute indistinct brown eyespots on the hindwing. The markings on the underside are less distinct and the dark brown stripe gives the butterfly a leaf-like appearance.

This butterfly is also commonly known as the Chocolate Soldier. It is fairly common in open country and on the forest edge at low elevations.

The caterpillar is dull dark brown in colour. It feeds on *Strobilanthes*, a dicotyledon plant.

## *Precis atlites* (Linnaeus)

GREY PANSY

This butterfly is coloured greyish buff, with the underside much paler. Both wings have dark brown irregular post-discal and submarginal lines, and a series of post-discal eyespots. Some of the eyespots are outwardly blackened and inwardly coloured orange.

The Grey Pansy is very common in the neighbourhood of villages and along forest roads. Although primarily a lowland butterfly, it is also found at higher elevations.

# *Precis almana* (Linnaeus)

## PEACOCK PANSY

This butterfly derives its common name from the prominent, white-eyed 'peacock' spot on the forewing, and a similar but much larger one at the apex on the hindwing. The upperside of the wings is coloured orange, while the underside is paler with additional eyespots.

The Peacock Pansy is very common in gardens and open country on the plains. It is not found on the hills.

# *Precis orithya* (Linnaeus)

BLUE PANSY

This butterfly exhibits sexual dimorphism. In the male, the forewing is black with a pale subapical band, two orange-red bars in the cell, and post-discal eyespots. The hindwing is bright blue, with an orange-red eyespot. The female has duller colours and also differs from the male in having two orange-red post-discal eyespots on the hindwing.

The Blue Pansy is generally found on grassy patches on the roadside and in open country on the plains. The male butterfly appears to be commoner than the female.

# *Kaniska canace* (Linnaeus)

BLUE ADMIRAL

This butterfly is coloured indigo blue above, with a broad paler blue post-discal band wings. The brownish black underside has a cryptic pattern resembling a dead leaf.

The Blue Admiral inhabits forested areas on the hills at higher elevations. It prefers open areas and may be found on flowers, on the path and on rocks in mid-stream in bright sunshine.

# *Symbrenthia hypatia* (Wallace)

INTRICATE JESTER

The two surfaces of the wings in this butterfly have very different colour patterns. The upperside is dark brown or black with orange bands, while the underside is pale buff richly variegated with reddish brown markings to give a marbled appearance.

This butterfly inhabits hilly areas at all usual elevations. It may be found visiting the sand-bank of jungle streams.

# *Rhinopalpa polynice* (Cramer)

WIZARD

This butterfly has a distinctive angled wing contour with a short tail on the hindwing. The upper surface of its wings is rich orange brown, with broad black margins and a series of black submarginal spots on the hindwing. The underside is dark purple brown, with fine wavy silvery blue lines and a full series of submarginal eyespots on both wings.

The Wizard inhabits well wooded localities at all usual elevations. It is, however, not common.

# *Hypolimnas anomala* (Wallace)

MALAYAN EGG-FLY

This is the commonest species of *Hypolimnas* in Malaysia. It was previously regarded as a subspecies of *H. antilope* (Cramer). The upper surface of its wings is dark brown with a slight gloss. There are two series of whitish submarginal spots on both wings.

The Malayan Egg-fly may be considered a poor mimic of one of the *Euploea* butterflies. It inhabits fairly open forest at low elevations.

## *Hypolimnas bolina* (Linnaeus)

GREAT EGG-FLY

This butterfly is represented by two subspecies in Peninsular Malaysia—the continental subspecies *jacintha* (Drury) and the insular subspecies *bolina* (Linnaeus). The two subspecies may be distinguished by the presence of white post-discal spots on the upper surface of the wings in *jacintha*. The female in both subspecies is variable, and more so in subspecies *bolina*.

The Great Egg-fly has been described as the most variable butterfly of the world. It has a strong flight and takes part in migratory flights. It may be found in gardens, secondary growth and on forest edge, primarily at low elevations.

## *Cyrestis themire* Honrath

LITTLE MAP-WING

This is the smallest species of *Cyrestis* butterflies and is formerly known as *C. periander* (Fabricius). Its wings are crossed by narrow orange-brown stripes, and are broadly bordered with greyish brown. It inhabits thick forest up to about 915 metres in altitude, but is very localised in distribution.

There are a number of other Map-wing butterflies in Malaysia. Of these, *C. lutea* (Zinken) is confined to the hills above 610 metres in altitude. The Marbled Map-wing *C. cocles* (Fabricius) is the rarest species, but may be found in open spaces in the vicinity of forest streams and quarries.

When in flight, these Map-wing butterflies look like pieces of paper blown by the wind.

*Cyrestis themire*

114

▲*Cyrestis lutea*                                    *Cyrestis cocles* ▼

# *Neptis hylas* (Linnaeus)

## COMMON SAILOR

This is the most abundant member of *Neptis* butterflies. It is common on all types of environments. Its wings are black and white above, while the underside is distinctively rich golden brown. It is, however, very variable, being made up of probably two separate geographical races in Malaysia.

There are a number of other black and white *Neptis* butterflies in Malaysia. Of these, the Malayan Sailor *N. duryodana* Moore and *N. leucoporos* Fruhstorfer are found in forest country at low elevations, while the Sullied Sailor *N. soma* Moore and *N. clinioides* de Nicéville occur in the hills.

▼*Neptis duryodana*

*Neptis hylas* ▶

*Neptis leucoporos*

▲ *Neptis duryodana*
◄ *Neptis soma*
▼ *Neptis clinioides*

## *Phaedyma columella* (Cramer)

### SHORT-BANDED SAILOR

This butterfly is rather similar to the black
and white *Neptis,* and was indeed previously
regarded as a species of the genus *Neptis.* It
prefers secondary growth and is common
near urban areas. It is larger than *Neptis
hylas* and differs in having the under surface
of the wings brown in colour.

## *Athyma perius* (Linnaeus)

### COMMON SERGEANT

This butterfly is similar to the black and
white *Neptis* in pattern and habits. The white
cell-streak on the forewing is, however,
divided into four parts. On the under surface
of the hindwing, the white post-discal fascia
has a proximal series of black spots.

The Common Sergeant inhabits secondary growth and open forest on the plains. It
may also visit gardens in urban areas.

## *Athyma nefte* (Cramer)

COLOUR SERGEANT

This butterfly exhibits sexual dimorphism. The female also occurs in two distinct forms. Both female forms appear to be commoner than the male.

This butterfly is common on the plains but rather rare on the hills. The female frequents *Lantana* flowers in open country.

## *Moduza procris* (Cramer)

COMMANDER

This butterfly is coloured dark reddish brown above, with a broad white macular discal band. The under surface of the wings is similarly marked as above, but the basal halves are greyish green.

The Commander inhabits forested areas on the plains, and is common in the vicinity of forest streams.

## *Lebadea martha* (Fabricius)

KNIGHT

This butterfly has a long and narrow forewing. The brownish wings are marked with a complex pattern, of which the narrow white discal band is diagnostic. It inhabits open forest on the plains.

## *Tanaecia pelea* (Fabricius)

MALAY VISCOUNT

This butterfly is coloured greyish brown above, with two dark zig-zag lines more or less filled in with white. The under surface of the wings is paler, with the distal half faintly tinged with violet.

The Malay Viscount inhabits primary forest, and is commoner at lower elevations.

## *Tanaecia lepidea* (Butler)

GREY COUNT

This butterfly is also formerly placed under the genus *Euthalia*. Unlike *Tanaecia iapis* and the like, the two sexes of the Grey Count are similar. The wings in the male are blackish brown, with a broad ashy grey marginal band. The female is larger and has a more buff-coloured hindwing margin.

The Grey Count inhabits forested hills above 760 metres in altitude. It is not an uncommon butterfly.

## *Tanaecia iapis* (Godart)

HORSFIELD'S BARON

This butterfly was formerly regarded as a species of the genus *Euthalia*. It is the most abundant member of *Tanaecia* in Malaysia.

The two sexes are differently coloured. In the male, the upperside is velvety black with a broad light blue marginal border. The female is coloured pale greyish brown, much as in *Tanaecia pelea*.

*Tanaecia godartii*

Male Horsfield's Baron may be easily confused with the much less common Malay Count *Tanaecia godartii* (G.R. Gray). *T. iapis* inhabits well-wooded localities at all elevations.

*Tanaecia iapis*

# *Lexias pardalis* (Moore)

ARCHDUKE

This butterfly exhibits sexual dimorphism. In the male, the upper surface of the wings is black with greenish blue margins on both wings, and a sprinkling of yellow spots on the forewing. The female is coloured dark brown above, with yellow spots on both wings.

*Lexias pardalis* (and other species) was formerly included in the genus *Euthalia*. It is essentially a jungle butterfly and is common at low elevations. It is replaced at higher elevations by a very similar species, *L. dirtea* (Fabricius). The two species can be separated by the colour of their antennal club—the apical portion is yellowish brown in *L. pardalis* but entirely black in *L. dirtea*.

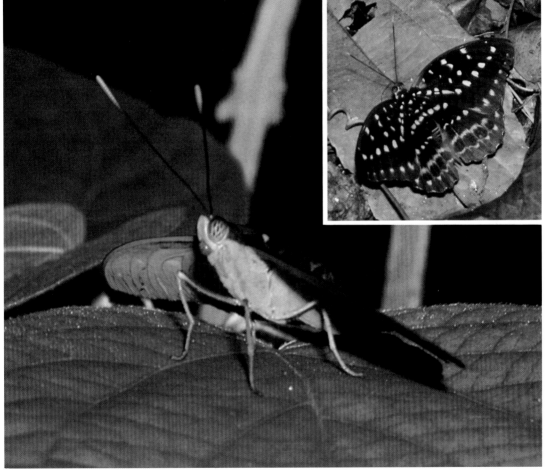

## *Bassarona teuta* (Doubleday)

BANDED MARQUIS

This butterfly was previously known as
*Euthalia teuta*. It appears to be rather rare
on mainland Malaysia where it occurs in
primary forest on the plains.

The two sexes are distinct. In the male, the
upper surface of the wings is blackish brown,
with a pale discal band running across both
wings. The female is much paler, and has a
series of dark zig-zag submarginal markings
and a distinctive discal band.

The Banded Marquis is variable in its
whitish markings. The two extreme forms in
Peninsular Malaysia are *B. teuta goodrichi*
(Distant) of the mainland and *B. teuta*
*rayana* Morishita which occurs in Langkawi
Islands. Intermediate forms are found in
Perlis and Kedah.

Two other species of this genus are
*Bassarona recta* (de Nicéville) and
*Bassarona dunya* (Doubleday). Both species
are not common.

## *Euthalia aconthea* (Cramer)

BARON

This butterfly is coloured dark brown above,
with white discal spots on the forewing and a
series of black submarginal spots on the
hindwing. The female is paler and larger
than the male.

The Baron inhabits primary forest on the
plains, but may also be found in orchards
and gardens. It is rather local in distribution.

The caterpillar is green in colour with a
yellow dorsal stripe. It has been found to
feed on *Anacardium occidentale* (cashew),
*Mangifera indica* (mango) and *Loranthus*
*scurrula*.

The butterflies in Langkawi Islands differ
from the mainland form in having more
contrasted colouring on the upper surface.

## *Euthalia monina* (Fabricius)

MALAY BARON

This is the commonest species of *Euthalia* in Malaysia. It occurs in primary forest at all usual elevations. The butterfly frequents rather damp, open areas especially around bamboo.

The male butterfly is represented by a number of well-defined forms. They are dark brown above, with the blue distal border on the hindwing bearing a series of dark zig-zag markings. The female resembles that sex of *Tanaecia iapis* but has a dark zig-zag line in the centre of the white post-discal band on the forewing.

The occurrence of different forms (polymorphism) of the Malay Baron attains its maximum in Borneo.

Although it is a common butterfly, its life history appears to be unknown.

## *Polyura jalysus* (C. & R. Felder)

INDIAN YELLOW NAWAB

The upper surface of the wings in this butterfly is greenish white, with a broad black apical border on the forewing. Most of the under surface is silvery green. This butterfly inhabits forested areas on the plains, and may be found drinking at the sand banks of forest streams.

The commonest member of the genus is the Common Nawab, *Polyura athamas* (Drury), which occurs in two distinct forms. The relationship of the two forms is uncertain although it has been suggested that they may belong to separate species.

The caterpillar of *P. athamas* has been reported to be secretive, feeding only at night on a variety of food plants, including *Acacia, Albizzia* and *Caesalpinia*.

# Family Riodinidae

THE butterflies comprising this family are commonly called 'Metalmarks' because of the presence on the wings of many species of small, metallic-looking flecks. They are remarkably variable in coloration and colour patterns.

Like the Beak butterflies, the forelegs of Metalmarks are imperfect and brush-like in the male but are functionally perfect in the female. The Beak butterflies have, in fact, been considered by some specialists to be related to the Metalmarks. However, the male genitalia of Metalmarks show a close affinity to those of the Lycaenidae. The caterpillars and chrysalids also bear some resemblance to those of the Lycaenidae. Indeed some specialists consider Metalmarks to be a subfamily of the Lycaenidae.

All Riodinid butterflies are practically confined to primary forest. They are usually found singly. In Malaysia, they characteristically settle on the upperside of leaves, with half-open wings. Elsewhere in the world, however, they have been described to rest typically on the under surface of a leaf, with their wings partly spread out.

Red Harlequin *Paralaxita telesia*

*Zemeros flegyas*

# *Zemeros flegyas* (Cramer)

## PUNCHINELLO

The Punchinello is a gay, little butterfly. It is represented by two forms in Malaysia. The mainland form occurs at all elevations but with a preference for the hills. It inhabits well-wooded localities and is often to be seen in the late afternoon on sunny days. It assumes a characteristic pose while at rest, with the wings half open and the hindwings held rather far forward.

Both sides of the wings are similarly coloured, but are paler on the underside as well as in the female. The deep reddish brown wings are marked with dark bands and submarginal spots. The forewing has a whitish subapical band, which is longer and more prominent in the female.

A similar looking species is *Z. emesoides* C. & R. Felder, which has similar habits but is more local in distribution. The wings are reddish or yellowish brown, with six dark brown bands.

*Zemeros flegyas*

*Zemeros emesoides*

126

*Zemeros emesoides*

## *Abisara saturata* (Moore)

MALAYAN PLUM JUDY

The two sexes of this butterfly have different markings on the wings. In the male, the upper surface is deep crimson brown without markings, while the underside is paler with a pair of diffuse post-discal bands on both wings and a series of black submarginal spots on the hindwing. The female is much paler and has in addition a diffuse white subapical patch on the forewing.

This butterfly inhabits primary and secondary forests at all elevations.

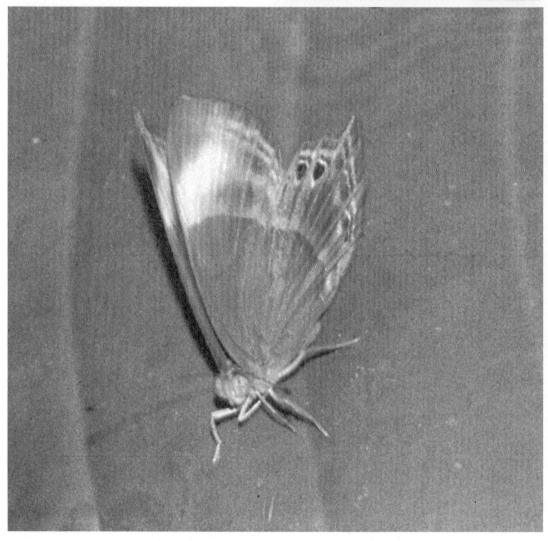

# *Paralaxita damajanti* (C. & R. Felder)

MALAY RED HARLEQUIN

This is one of the prettiest Malaysian butterflies. The wings are coloured rich carmine, unmarked above but beautifully ornamented with blue-edged black spots on the under surface.

This butterfly inhabits dense forests up to moderate elevations on the hills. It was formerly placed under the genus *Laxita*.

Two other Malaysian species are *P. orphana* (Boisduval) and *P. telesia* (Hewitson).

## *Laxita thuisto* (Hewitson)

LESSER HARLEQUIN

This butterfly was previously known as *Taxila thuisto*. The two sexes can be distinguished by their coloration. The male is black above, while the female is reddish brown with black spots and a white subapical fascia on the forewing. The under surface is orange brown ornamented with blue-edged black spots.

The Lesser Harlequin occurs in well-wooded localities and is commoner at lower elevations. Another species, *L. teneta,* does not occur in Peninsular Malaysia.

# *Taxila haquinus* (Fabricius)

HARLEQUIN

The under surface of the wings in this butterfly is coloured orange brown, ornamented with outwardly blue-edged black spots. The male is dark brown above, with orange brown apex on the forewing. The upper surface in the female is pale reddish brown, with a white apical band on the forewing.

This butterfly inhabits forested areas at lower elevations. Its life history is unknown.

The Harlequin looks rather like *Laxita* and *Paralaxita* butterflies.

# Family Lycaenidae

MEMBERS of this family are characterised by their metallic colours, quick flight and great fondness for the sunshine. They are commonly known as Blues, Coppers and Hairstreaks. In Malaysia, over one-third of the butterfly fauna belong to this family. It is generally believed that more species are yet to be discovered. The majority of them inhabit primeval forest, but quite a number of them are common in gardens and by the roadside.

Many Lycaenid butterflies are brilliantly coloured with iridescent blue, violet, green, red, orange or brown. The upper surface of the wings is often very differently coloured between the sexes. It is also almost invariably quite different from the pattern of the under surface. Usually, the female is duller and of more sombre colouring. In some instances, sex dimorphism is so marked that the two sexes have been regarded as different species.

The colours in Lycaenid butterflies are not due to pigments but are of the type known as structural colours, *i.e.* they are due to the light falling onto the wings being sorted out into its different wave lengths by the process known as 'interference'. The effect is produced by ultra-microscopic grooves, ridges or other structural features on the scales.

Many Lycaenid butterflies are ornamented with 1–3 pairs of filamentous 'tails' on the hindwing. In addition, they have an eyespot at the base of this hindwing tail. When the butterfly is at rest with its wings over its back, this combination of eyespot and tail makes the butterfly appear to face the opposite direction to the actual position. This illusion is further enhanced by the characteristically quivering tails looking like the antennae. Thus the predator is deluded into thinking the back is the front, and peck at an unessential rather than a vital part of the butterfly.

*Drupadia theda*

The forelegs of Lycaenid butterflies are reduced in size compared with the mid- and hind-legs. The eyes are placed close together, as in the Riodinidae. Likewise, the early stages differ from those of other families both in their morphology and in their widespread association with ants.

Lycaenid caterpillars are quite distinctive, being typically short, stout and slug-like, or woodlouse-shaped. A large number of species apparently enjoy a symbiotic relationship with ants. These species possess 'honeydew' glands in the abdomen. In most species, a single opening is connected with the gland, but in the case of the Coppers the sweet secretion is exuded all over the body. The sweet secretion is greatly relished by ants, which commonly attend the caterpillars and often defend them against enemies. Some ants even carry such caterpillars into their nests as 'guests'.

Although principally plant-feeders, the caterpillars of some species may feed on other insects, such as aphids, scale insects and leaf-hoppers. Some may even invade ant nests and prey on ant larvae. In addition, the Blue caterpillars may often be cannibalistic, devouring their fellows until only one is left on each leaf or flower head.

*Celastrina camenae*

*Deramas jasoda*

## *Allotinus leogoron* Fruhstorfer

Butterflies of the genus *Allotinus* are easily recognised by the whitish or pale buff under surface which is densely speckled with brown streaks and spots. *A. leogoron* has a whiter ground colour, and neater and darker brown markings than related species. It inhabits lowland jungle and is not common.

*Allotinus apries*

*Allotinus leogoron*

## *Everes lacturnus* (Godart)

INDIAN CUPID

This butterfly inhabits forested areas on the plains and in the foothills, and occurs sporadically in rather open country.

In the male the upper surface of the wings is pale purple-blue, with dark margins. The female is dark brown with orange tornal eyespots. The underside is pale grey, with brown post-discal spots on both wings and black subbasal and submarginal spots on the hindwing. The submarginal spots are proximally orange crowned.

The caterpillar is green in colour, with black dorsal and subdorsal lines, a light lateral line and dark spiracles. Its food plants include the legume *Trifolium*.

The Indian Cupid is distributed throughout the Oriental Region and reaches Australia.

134

# *Caleta roxus* (Godart)

## STRAIGHT PIERROT

This and other Pierrot butterflies were formerly placed under the genus *Castalius*. They are often found settled at moist places on forest paths and stream banks at low elevations.

The upper wing surface of *C. roxus* is predominantly black, with a broad white discal band. The underside is white, with a straight black subbasal band, a series of conjoined post-discal spots, and black marginal fasciae.

A very similar species, the Elbowed Pierrot *C. elna* (Hewitson), differs in having an angled subbasal band.

Caleta roxus

Caleta elna

# *Celastrina puspa* (Horsfield)

COMMON HEDGE BLUE

This butterfly has a distinctive underside pattern. In the male the upper surface is shining blue, with narrow black borders and white discal patches on both wings. The female is pale shining greenish blue, with broad black border on the forewing and with the distal half of the hindwing dark dusted.

The Common Hedge Blue is common along forest paths in the lowlands, and may be found drinking at moist places.

Most of the *Celastrina* butterflies occur in the hills. An easily recognised species is *C. carna* (de Nicéville), in which the forewing post-discal markings on the under surface are particularly heavy and black.

Celastrina carna

Celastrina puspa

# *Jamides celeno* (Cramer)

COMMON CAERULEAN

This butterfly is very widely distributed and abundant. It occurs in gardens, secondary growth and open forest at elevations below about 1220 metres.

The upper surface of the wings is whitish blue, with a broad black border on the forewing in the male. The underside has a single subbasal pair of striaght white lines on the hindwing.

## *Chilades pandava* (Horsfield)
CYCAD BLUE

This butterfly is sometimes common in urban gardens and secondary growth. Its caterpillar feeds on cycad *(Cycas revoluta)* and other plants, and is attended by ants.

The hindwing in this butterfly is tailed and the tornal spots on the underside are orange-crowned. In the male the upper surface is coloured blue, with narrow black borders and a black tornal spot on the hindwing. The female is paler blue, with a broad border on the forewing and submarginal spots on the hindwing.

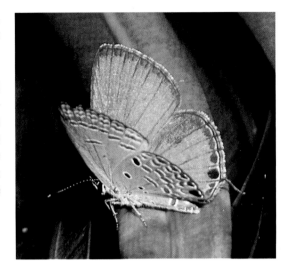

## *Nacaduba beroe* (C. & R. Felder)
SIX-LINE BLUE

This butterfly is distinguished from other six-line Blues in having the area between the fine post-discal lines on the underside uniformly coloured as the ground colour of the wings.

Like other six-line Blues (*berenice* group), the underside forewing has a pair of subbasal lines across the cell. This feature is not found in the four-line Blues (*pavana* group).

The upperside of this butterfly is purple in the male. The upperside forewing of the female has a purple-blue patch and bluish spots.

The greyish brown underside has the usual Lycaenine pattern with pairs of whitish lines. The wing bases are darkened in the male. The hindwing has a black marginal spot with an orange crown.

*Nacaduba beroe* is widely distributed in Peninsular Malaysia. It is found in the plains as well as the hills.

Other six-line Blues are *Nacaduba berenice* (Herrich-Schaffer), *N. kurava* (Moore) and *N. calauria* (C. Felder).

## *Anthene emolus* (Godart)

CILIATE BLUE

The under surface of this butterfly is pale earthy brown, with a series of whitish stripes on both wings and an orange-crowned black spot on the hindwing. In the male the upper surface is deep purple blue. The female is dull brown, with purple wing bases and dark marginal spots on the hindwing.

This is the most widespread *Anthene* butterfly and occurs at all usual elevations.

## *Arhopala athada* (Staudinger)

The male butterfly is violet blue above, with narrow borders. The female is purple blue with wide borders. The under surface is brown with numerous spots and bands.

This butterfly inhabits lowland forest. It has been confused with another very similar-looking species, *A. zambra* Swinhoe. Indeed members of this genus are quite similar and very hard to distinguish from one another.

## *Una usta* (Distant)

SINGLETON

The Singleton is a monotypic butterfly; it is the only species of the genus *Una*. It occurs from Assam to Sundaland.

This tailless butterfly appears to be nowhere common in Peninsular Malaysia. The female is reported to be very rare, while the male is commoner. The life history is not known.

The upperside of the male butterfly is deep brownish purple, while that of the female is pale purplish blue. It has broad brown borders.

The underside of this butterfly is pale buff brown, with post-discal and submarginal spots on both wings. The hindwings also possess dark spots on the basal and costal areas.

# *Spindasis lohita* (Horsfield)

## LONG-BANDED SILVERLINE

Butterflies of the genus *Spindasis* are easily recognised by the silvery markings on the underside and the two hindwing tails.

In *S. lohita* the upper surface of the wings is brown with an orange tornal area on the hindwing. The underside is yellow, with 5 or 6 silver lines broadly edged with dark red or more rarely black. This butterfly is common in secondary growth and along forest edge below about 790 metres in altitude. Above 790 metres it is replaced by a similar but larger species, *S. seliga* (Fruhstorfer).

Another common Silverline butterfly is the Club Silverline *S. syama* (Horsfield). It is as common as *S. lohita* and inhabits the same areas. It is best separated from *S. lohita* by the shape of the basal streak on the forewing below; it is club-like in *S. syama* but L-shaped in *S. lohita*.

*Spindasis lohita*

*Spindasis syama*

139

## *Loxura cassiopeia* Distant

### LARGER YAMFLY

This butterfly is very similar to the Yamfly *L. atymnus* (Stoll), of which it is often being confused. The upper surface of its wings is reddish orange, with a black apical border on the forewing that continues along the costa. The underside is yellowish buff, with a somewhat obscure dislocated post-discal band.

*L. cassiopeia* is a forest butterfly that occurs up to 790 metres in altitude.

## *Eooxylides tharis* (Geyer)

### BRANDED IMPERIAL

This butterfly is coloured dark brown above, with black confluent spots in the white tornal patch on the hindwing. The underside is reddish orange, with large black submarginal spots in the white tornal area on the hindwing. There are three hindwing tails.

The Branded Imperial is somewhat local in distribution, but may be found along forest paths at all usual elevations.

## *Cheritra freja* (Fabricius)

### COMMON IMPERIAL

The hindwing of this butterfly has two tails. The upper surface is brownish purple in the male, but dark brown in the female. The white tornal area on the hindwing has large black spots. The underside is white, with most of the forewing and the apical area of the hindwing shaded orange-brown, a post-discal line on both wings, and black submarginal line and tornal spots on the hindwing.

This butterfly inhabits lowland forest at low to moderate elevations.

## *Drupadia ravindra* (Horsfield)

COMMON POSY

This butterfly exhibits considerable variation. It inhabits wooded areas and has a swift darting flight.

In the male the upper surface is coloured dark brown on the forewing and azure blue on the hindwing. The female is dark brown with traces of orange discal patch on the forewing, and a marginal series of black spots on the bluish grey tornal area of the hindwing.

The underside is coloured orange on the forewing. The hindwing is mostly white, marked with solid black bands and spots.

## *Hypolycaena erylus* (Godart)

COMMON TIT

The Common Tit is a common butterfly. It occurs from the coast to the forested hills. It is frequently seen on moist spots of forest roads.

The upperside of the male butterfly is deep purple in colour, while that of the female is dull brown.

The greyish underside has a reddish brown post-discal line on both wings. The apical and marginal areas are shaded ochreous brown. The hindwing has two black tornal spots, one of which is orange-crowned.

The caterpillar is green in colour. It is attended by ants.

It has been suggested that the Common Tit be assigned to another genus as its genitalia differ from those of typical *Hypolycaena*.

A similar-looking species is *Hypolycaena thecloides* (C. & R. Felder). This can be distinguished by the presence of an orange tornal area on the upperside of the hindwing, and the presence of a prominent orange bar at the base of space 7 of the underside hindwing.

# Family Hesperiidae

MEMBERS of the Hesperiidae are quite distinct from the true butterflies. They are often regarded as 'in between' butterflies and moths. They are, however, more closely related to the butterflies than other Lepidopterans.

Adult Hesperiid butterflies have a large head and stout, hairy body with relatively small, often pointed, wings and 3 pairs of well-developed legs. Their eyes are large and protruding. The antennae are clubbed like those of the true butterflies, but are often bent backwards at the apex giving a slightly hooked appearance. Unlike the true butterflies, all the wing veins arise either from the base of the wing or from the cell.

Hesperiid butterflies are fast fliers, but the flight is short and not sustained. Their characteristic darting flight bestows them the common name of 'Skippers'. They are also sometimes known as Awls or Dusky-wings.

Most Skipper butterflies are rather plainly coloured with browns and tawny yellows. The markings when present on the upperside are usually confined to the forewing. Often, there is little or no difference in the wing pattern between related species, thus making identification difficult or impossible without examining the genitalia.

Many Skippers are sun-loving, and may be seen darting around flowering plants such as *Lantana* and *Cordia*. Most of them are active only in the early morning and at dusk; some may, however, fly during midday in shadier parts of the forest.

The Skipper caterpillars are usually stout, and may be naked or with dispersed bristles. Some of them feed on monocotyledonous plants (palms, grasses, bamboos, bananas, gingers), while others feed on dicotyledons.

*Potanthus rectifasciata*

In many species the caterpillars fasten leaves of the food plant together with silk to form a rolled-up shelter to live in. These caterpillars appear to feed only at night.

Unlike the true butterflies, the chrysalids of the Hesperiidae are usually enclosed in rather flimsy silken cocoons or in rolled leaves fastened with silk.

In Malaysia, the 250 or so Hesperiid species so far recorded is probably an underestimate. Like the Lycaenidae, many new discoveries may be expected from this family.

*Celaenorrhinus aurivittatus*

*Salanoemia similis*

## *Celaenorrhinus aurivittatus* (Moore)

### DARK YELLOW-BANDED FLAT

This butterfly is coloured chocolate brown, with a yellow discal band and three conjoined or separated subapical spots on the forewing. It is rather local in distribution, but is not uncommon in fairly open forest at all usual elevations.

## *Tagiades gana* (Moore)

### LARGE SNOW FLAT

This is the commonest species of *Tagiades* in Malaysia. It occurs in both primary and secondary forests at moderate elevations.

The upper surface is dark brown, with rather obscure darker discal and post-discal spots. There are 3 white hyaline subapical spots on the forewing. The tornal area of the hindwing is white with diffuse black spots.

Another common species is the Common Snow Flat *T. japetus* (Stoll), which has no white tornal area on the hindwing.

The Snow Flat butterflies are sun-loving. They settle with their wings fully outspread.

*Tagiades japetus*

*Tagiades gana*

144

## *Halpe ormenes* (Plotz)

This and other *Halpe* butterflies have a white spot on the antennal club just before the apiculus. Their wing surfaces are coloured brown, with small white hyaline spots on the forewing.

*H. ormenes* is characterised by the possession of an almost clear-white and regular discal band on the hindwing. It is closely related to a similar species, the Banded Ace *H. zema* (Hewitson).

## *Koruthaialos sindu* (C. & R. Felder)

BRIGHT RED VELVET BOB

This butterfly is coloured dark brown on both wings, with a red discal band on the forewing; the discal band is paler and broader in the female. It inhabits primary forest at all elevations.

## *Notocrypta paralysos* (Wood-Mason & de Nicéville)

BANDED DEMON

This butterfly is coloured black on both wing surfaces, with a white hyaline discal band on the forewing. It inhabits primary and secondary lowland forests.

## *Isma umbrosa* (Elwes & Edwards)

This butterfly is coloured dark brown above, with white hyaline post-discal spots on the forewing. The prominent discal spots on the upperside hindwing in the male are either quadrate or elongate. The female has at least one spot on the upperside hindwing.

*I. umbrosa* is extremely variable in the extent of the spotting and colouring on certain parts of the wing surfaces. Indeed identification of *Isma* butterflies has proved difficult because of the similarity between species, diversity between the sexes, and marked individual variation.

## *Zela onara* (Butler)

This butterfly was formerly placed under the genus *Lotongus*. The genus *Zela* has a very short hindwing cell, yellow or orange hindwing tornal cilia, and red eyes. Like *Lotongus, Zela* butterflies are generally known as Palmers.

*Z. onara* has a narrow, curved, black stigma on the inner edge of the hyaline spot in space 2 of the upperside forewing. The broad pale yellow discal band on the underside hindwing reaches the dorsum just above the tornus.

This butterfly is not common and is confined to lowland forest.

## *Salanoemia similis* (Elwes & Edwards)

This butterfly was formerly known as *Plastingia similis*. The genus *Salanoemia* differs from *Plastingia* in the possession of symmetrical genitalia, and concolorous veins and rounded post-discal spots on the underside hindwing.

*S. similis* has a yellow discal area on the upperside forewing, with or without a very small cell spot. It inhabits wooded areas but is not common.

## *Eetion elia* (Hewitson)

This is the only species of the genus *Eetion*. It inhabits lowland primary forest, but is not common.

The wings are coloured dark brown, with white hyaline spots. The basal half of the underside hindwing is silvery white. The abdomen is dark brown with white bands, and entirely white beneath.

## *Oriens goloides* (Moore)

This butterfly is very similar to the Common Dartlet *O. gola* (Moore), but its veins across the yellow bands are heavily blackened. It inhabits secondary growth on the plains.

The wings are dark brown above, with orange-yellow post-discal bands. The forewing costa is dusted with orange-yellow. The underside is ochreous, with rather obscure black spotting indicating approximately the upperside markings.

## *Potanthus omaha* (W.H. Edwards)

LESSER DART

This butterfly was formerly known as *Padraona maesoides* (Butler). It is widely distributed and is common on the plains.

The wings are dark brown above, with bright orange-yellow markings divided by dark veins. The under surface is black, with markings as above. The costal half of the forewing and the whole of the hindwing are, however, rather heavily dusted with yellowish scales.

# SCHEMATIC DIAGRAM OF THE BUTTERFLY WINGS

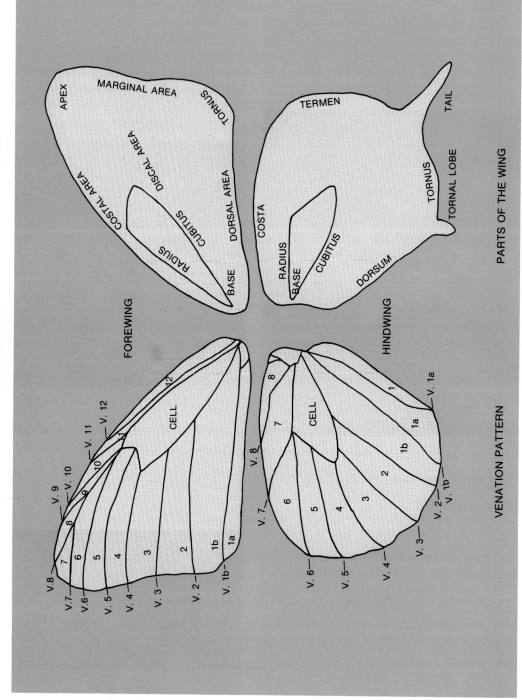

PARTS OF THE WING

VENATION PATTERN

# Index

Page numbers in *italics* indicate illustrations.